Design and Make Simple Structures
& Fairground Models
Adrienne Dawes

Introduction

Structures are all around us and most children will have enjoyed the experience of a fairground ride. These experiences make the activities featured in this booklet appropriate for all pupils because of their first hand involvement. When the basic techniques have been introduced to the pupils and they have been given time to experiment with a range of materials then the teacher must ensure that:

• The project / task given to the pupils is demanding enough to allow them to perform at a higher level.
• The task is interesting so that the pupils are encouraged to persist.
• A variety of equipment is available to ensure appropriate choices can be made.
• All equipment and materials are available in the class and they are easily accessible so as to ensure pupils make the correct decisions.
• Sufficient time is allowed to enable thorough experimentation by individuals so that they can practice newly acquired skills, be taught how to correctly use any new pieces of equipment, develop ideas and apply finishing techniques.
• The teacher has the skills and knowledge necessary to intervene when appropriate.

Experimentation and choice on the part of the pupils is very important. This book contains photocopiable resources and teacher / pupil instructions, which will enable you to teach and practice a variety of skills and techniques appropriate to the making of Simple Structures and Fairground rides. The activities are designed to assist adults when introducing new techniques to Key Stage one and Key Stage two pupils and when used by a whole school will aid progression. The activities are intended to be used as an introduction and when the pupils have completed these introductory activities they should be provided with a range of materials and equipment to enable them to apply their skills in a Design and Make task and create their own Structures and Fairground Rides. Specific skills and techniques that the children need to be taught to complete the models are identified during each activity. There are opportunities during the making of the models and their extension activities to test the structures and movement of rides, simple mechanisms and some simple electrical circuits.

Cont

Background Information..............................2

Key Stage 1 Models
Beam Bridge...4
Pillars...6
Towers..8
Tents...10
Simple Picture Frame..............................12
Woven Basket...14
Woven Fabric Wall Hanging...................16
Model Chair...18
Lifting Drawbridge.................................20
Wind Powered Dodgems.........................22
Tin Can Roundabout................................24
Slide...26
Helter Skelter..28
Paper Carrier Bag....................................30

Tools and Techniques..............................32

Key Stage 2 Models
Tower...34
Crane..36
Pylon..38
Box Container..40
Model House..42
Supporting Structure...............................44
Swingboat..46
Death Plank...48
Big Wheel..50
Octopus Ride...52
Umbrella Ride...54
Merry-Go-Round.....................................56
Roundabout..58
Rising, Falling & Turning Roundabout...........60
Paper Drinks Container............................62
Fairground Art...64

Illustrated by Adrienne Dawes and Paul Sealey
Printed in Great Britain for "Topical Resources", Publishers of Educational Materials, P.O. Box 329, Broughton, Preston. PR3 5LT
(Tel/Fax 01772 863158)
by T. Snape & Co. Ltd., Boltons Court, Preston.
Cover Design: Paul Sealey Illustration & Design

First Published May 1998
ISBN 1 872977 31 6

Background Information

The world is full of structures. Some are natural e.g. a tree, spider's web, honeycomb, leaf, birds' nest, wasps' nest. Some are manufactured e.g. a house, car, chair, crane, paper bag, fishing net, woollen jumper. Within the areas of natural and manufactured structures there are two different types of structures:

Frame Structures

e.g. suspension bridge, crane, pylon, honeycomb, leaf, kite, tent, skeleton, bicycle, slide, swing, woven fabrics. These are made by strips of material joined together which are either hidden by a 'skin' or left exposed. Triangulation is the main method of strengthening these structures.

Shell Structures

e.g. house, drinks carton, paper bag, snails' shells, eggs, margarine tubs. These are held together by their 'skin' - the material of which they are made. Shell structures can be strengthened by altering the shape of the material, incorporating folds and bends or by adding ribs to the structure. Often structures consist of a frame and a shell structure creating strength. e.g. our bodies [skeleton and skin]

A structure must support its own weight and whatever object / weight / load is placed on it or in it. If a structure collapses it is called structural failure. Strengthening a structure is known as stabilizing a structure. Once children have a basic understanding of structures they can apply this knowledge to creating frames to supprt mechanisms.

Fairgrounds are a magical world of movement, colour, sound and light and because they are such a stimulating environment they can encourage childrens imagination and by applying taught skills and knowledge and understanding of structures and forces the children can create models of their favourite rides or models that demonstrate certain types of movement e.g. swinging, sliding, spinning.

Children must be aware of different types of structures and how they can be strengthened and made more stable when developing designs for their rides. Children should either visit a fairground or watch a video that features a variety of rides before the activity takes place. If this is not possible then a visit to a local playground will show the pupils a variety of rides that could be turned into spectacular fairground attractions which are strong enough to do the job for which they were intended. The creation of fairground rides can be linked to free and investigative work with construction kits and appropriate references are made to these activities during the design and make projects.

Because Fairground art is bright and decorative, special care should be taken when finishings are applied and suggestions for designs are include in the booklet. All fairground rides provide a thrill or sensation and the completed models should be both visually attractive and exciting in action.

Structures

There are many natural and manufacturd structures in the world around us. Which of these structures are natural and which are manufactured? Write underneath the pictures 'n' for natural and 'm' for manufactured:

Brick Walls

Honeycomb

Fishing Rod

Spiders'Web

Snail Shell

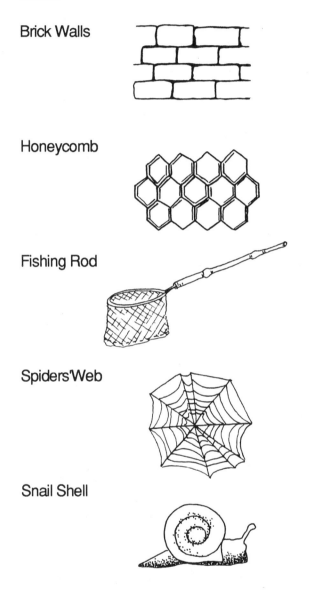

Write on the lines which are shell structures and which are frame structures:

Shell Structures | Frame Structures

Collect pictures of many different types of structures and categorise them as either natural or manufactured by man or woman, frame structures, shell structures or both.

The Programmes of Study for Design and Technology state that at Key Stage 1 pupils should be taught:
• how to make their structures more stable and withstand greater loads. In doing this they should be given opportunities to:
• make different types of structures e.g. walls, towers, frameworks
• become familiar with simple ways of making structures more stable e.g. widening the base
• become familiar with simple ways of strengthening structures e.g. using tubes, props and buttresses.

At Key Stage 2 pupils should be taught:
• how structures can fail when loaded, and techniques for reinforcing and strengthening them. In doing this they should be given opportunities to:
•become familiar with some different types of structures e.g. arches, frames, shells,woven etc.
•become familiar with simple ways of strengthening and reinforcing structures e.g.ribbing, corrugated and adding gussets.

Use construction kits such as Plastc Meccano or BrioMec or teacher prepared strips of card to create rectangular frames. Fasten the corners with paper fasteners. star fasteners or nuts and bolts as in the diagram. Is the structure stable? How can the structure be strengthened?Add an extra strip diagonally across the structure.

Test the structure again. What has happened? Why?

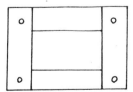

Use construction kits to create brick walls. Experiment with patterns. Which pattern of bricks make the strongest wall?

Beam Bridge

Technique used:

Strengthening paper to create beam bridges and testing to destruction.

Equipment needed:

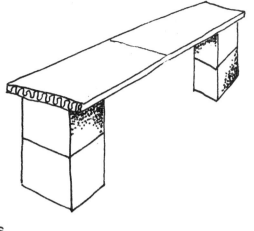

scissors glue
artstraws building blocks
sellotape sugar paper
reclaimed corrugated card

How to make the example:

Step 1. Photocopy the sheet opposite twice, one set per group of children.

Step 2. Cut out the 2 photocopies of each bridge surface and glue onto the surfaces as directed, end to end as in the diagram. **N.B. The surfaces onto which the photocopied bridge surfaces are glued must be 50cms long in one piece.**

Step 3. Using building blocks, make 2 towers for supports. They should be about 30 cm's apart.

Step 4. Place the corrugated card bridge across the supports and fasten across the top of the building blocks using sellotape.
Test the strength of the bridge by placing weights gently in the middle.
Record the results in a table and continue adding weights until the bridge collapses.

Step 5. Now test the other two bridges in the same way, using the same weights and record the results.

Step 6. Discuss which is the strongest bridge.

How the idea may be developed:

Test the bridges with other groups using toy cars or play people. Place the weights in the middle of the bridges. What happens? Place the weights at the end of the bridges. What happens? Where are the bridge's weakest parts? Make a pillar out of rolled up card and place it under the middle of the beam bridges. The pillar must be the same height as the building block supports. Test again. What happens this time. Why? Create a beam bridge by rolling pieces of newspaper into tubes and glue them onto a sheet of newspaper as in the diagram. Test the strength of this beam bridge. Newspaper can be made stronger by coating it evenly in a mixture of flour and water. Allow the coating to dry before testing the strengthened paper.Try strengthening the bridge by using pieces of card folded in different ways as in the diagram. To ensure the tests are fair, all the pieces of card must be the same size.

weights	artstraw bridge	sugar paper bridge	corrugated card bridge
45gms			
35gms	✓		
25gms	✓		✓
15gms	✓		✓
5gm	✓	X	✓

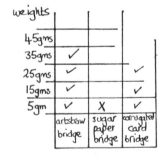

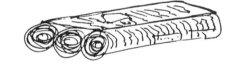

A

glue onto thick corrugated
reclaimed card

B

glue artstraws onto
the underside

C

glue onto sugar paper

Pillars

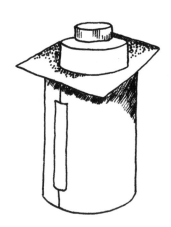

Technique used:

Changing the shape of paper and testing the strength of different shaped shell structures.

Stress is the amount of force you put on a structure. Strain is how much the structure changes when you put stress on it.

Equipment needed:

scissors	weights	glue stick
paper	sticky tape	card

How to make the example:

Step 1. Photocopy the sheet opposite, one per pair of children or group.
Step 2. Cut out the rectangular pieces of paper along the solid black lines.
Step 3. Roll the round pillar shape and glue in place. Fold the other pieces along the broken black lines and glue in place to create pillars as in the diagram below:

    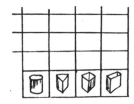

Step 4. Place a flat piece of card on top of each of the pillars - the card on each pillar must be the same size to ensure a fair test.
Step 5. Place weights on the pillars and record the results on a chart as in the diagram.
Step 6. Test the pillars to destruction.

How the idea may be developed:

The pupils can use equal sized pieces of paper and roll them to create pillars of varying diameters. Test the pillars and record the results. How was the strongest pillar made? Does the length of the pillar make any difference to the results?

Let the pupils experiment with making a pontoon bridge. Tests must be carried out on floating and sinking prior to the bridges being made. The children could use lolly sticks, twigs or polystyrene trays.

overlap tab A here and tape

round pillar

A

overlap tab A here and tape

triangular pillar

A

overlap tab A here and tape

square pillar

A

overlap tab A here and tape

rectangular pillar

A

© **Topical Resources**. May be photocopied for classroom use only.

Towers

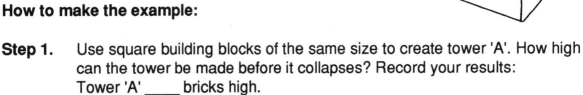

Technique used:

Building towers to test their stability.

Equipment needed:

building blocks	card
artstraws	pipe cleaners
sticky tape	reclaimed boxes

How to make the example:

Step 1. Use square building blocks of the same size to create tower 'A'. How high can the tower be made before it collapses? Record your results:
Tower 'A' _____ bricks high.
Tower 'A' _____ cms high.

Step 2. Use building blocks or reclaimed boxes to create tower 'B'. How high can the tower be made before it collapses? Record your results:
Tower 'B' _____ cuboids high.
Tower 'B' _____ cms high.

Step 3. Use toilet roll tubes and sheets of card to create tower 'C'. How high can the tower be made before it collapses? Record your results:
Tower 'C' _____ tubes high.
Tower 'C' _____ cms high.

Step 4. Use toilet roll tubes and sheets of card to create tower 'D'. How high can the tower be made before it collapses? Record your results:
Tower 'D' _____ tubes high.
Tower 'D' _____ cms high.

Step 5. Use art straws and pipecleaners to create tower 'E'. How high can the tower be made before it collapses? Record your results:
Tower 'E' _____ artstraws high.
Tower 'E' _____ cms high.

Step 6. Use rolled up newspapers to create tower 'F'. How high can the tower be made before it collapses? Record your results:
Tower 'F' _____ tubes high.
Tower 'F' _____ cms high.

Step 7. Photocopy the sheet opposite, one per group of children.
Fill in the appropriate spaces next to the tower illustrations.

How the idea may be developed.

Collect pictures of towers and display them with pupils towers and recording sheets. Can the pupils create their own towers using frame structures? Try artstraws, plastic straws, rolled up sugar paper, strips of card. Try creating towers using construction kits: e.g. Lasy, Meccano, BrioMec etc.

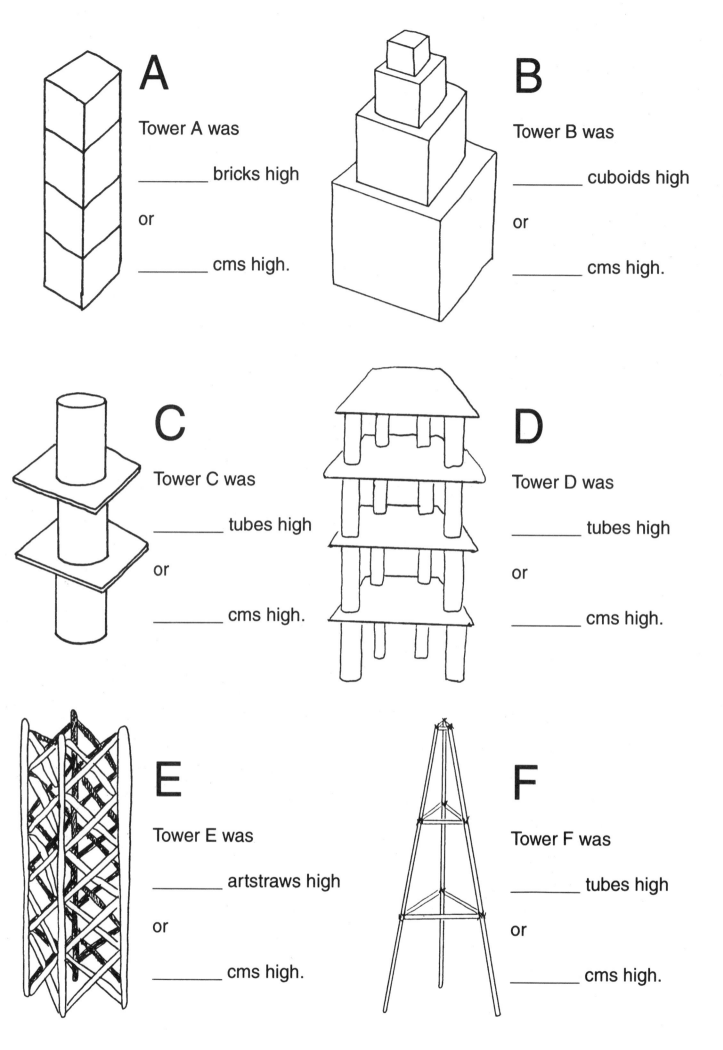

A

Tower A was

_____ bricks high

or

_____ cms high.

B

Tower B was

_____ cuboids high

or

_____ cms high.

C

Tower C was

_____ tubes high

or

_____ cms high.

D

Tower D was

_____ tubes high

or

_____ cms high.

E

Tower E was

_____ artstraws high

or

_____ cms high.

F

Tower F was

_____ tubes high

or

_____ cms high.

Tents

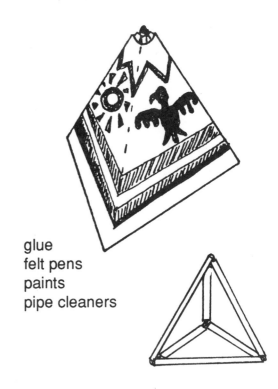

Technique used:

Straw frame structures covered in
fabric shells - pattern making.

Equipment needed:

thin plastic straws or artstraws	glue
utility snips	felt pens
sticky tape	paints
plain fabric	pipe cleaners

How to make the example:

Step 1. Cut 6 straws using scissors so that they measure 10 cm in length.

Step 2. Using the utility snips, cut 8 pieces of pipe cleaner measuring 5cm in length.

Step 3. Using one piece of pipe cleaner, push it into the ends of 2 straws. Bend the pipe cleaner and continue adding straws and pipe cleaner joiners until you have created the structure in the diagram.

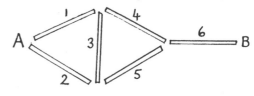

Step 4. Raise straw 6 at the end marked B and then raise the apex of the triangle 'A'. Fasten together the 2 points to form a pyramid with 3 equal sides.

Step 5. Photocopy the sheet opposite, one per child.

Step 6. Cut out the pattern for the covering of the pyramid tent around the solid black lines.

Step 7. Pin the pattern to a piece of plain fabric and cut the fabric to the correct size.

Step 8. Remove the pins and the paper pattern and let the pupils decorate the fabric using felt pens or pencil crayons.

Step 9. Attach the covering to the pyramid using either sticky tape or glue.

Step 10. Test the strength of the tent structure by either blowing on it or use a balloon pump. (If a hairdryer is used then this must be under adult supervision.)

How the idea may be developed:

Cut out the conical tent pattern from the photocopied sheet and decorate the paper pattern using either felt pens or crayons. Glue along the tab to form a conical shape. Test the strength of this tent structure. How can the pupils ensure a fair test? Make some other covered frame tents and test them. Which shape is the best?

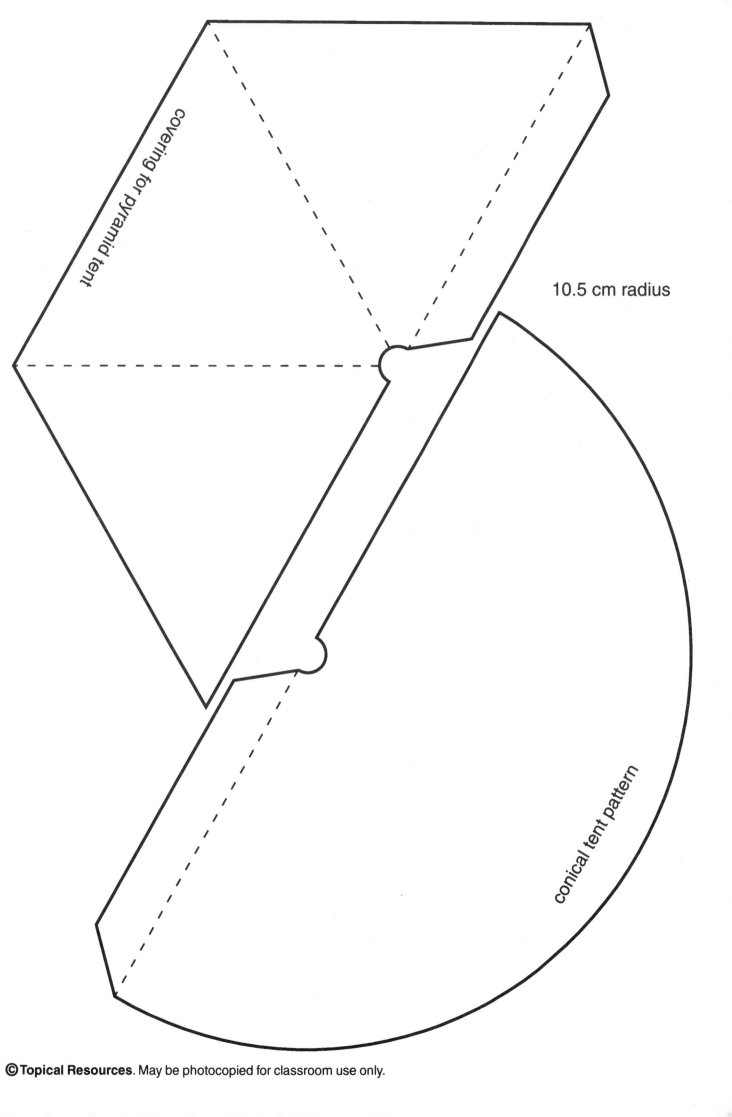

covering for pyramid tent

10.5 cm radius

conical tent pattern

Simple Picture Frame

Technique used:

Square section wood and card triangles.

Equipment needed:

scissors	glue
reclaimed card	hack saw
1cm square section wood	bench hook

How to make the example:

Step 1. Photocopy the sheet opposite, one per child.

Step 2. Cut out one rectangle and paste to square section wood. Using the rectangle as a template, cut the wood to 9cm long.

Step 3. Repeat step 2 three times to give you four 9cm strips of wood. Tidy the ends of the sawn wood with sandpaper if necessary.

Step 4. Cut out "picture frame shape" and paste to reclaimed card. (Old greetings cards are ideal for this.)

Step 5. Use P.V.A. to glue square section wood in the dotted shapes shown on the "picture frame shape". Allow at least five minutes to become firm.

Step 6. Cut out triangles and paste to reclaimed card.

Step 7. Glue card triangles over each corner joint (as shown in the diagram) using P.V.A. glue.

Step 8. Decorate the picture frame with paints or felt tipped pens.

Step 9. Finally, cut a picture from a glossy magazine or an old photograph and glue inside the frame.

How the idea may be developed:

This simple design can be developed in a number of different ways. The dimensions may be changed to make larger or smaller frames, the frames may be decorated with printing or marbling techniques and the chosen picture could be varnished to give a "glass like" effect. The hanging bracket at the top may be removed and pupils asked to experiment with different ways of hanging the frame from behind. Alternatively, simple supporting brackets can be invented to enable the frame to become free standing.

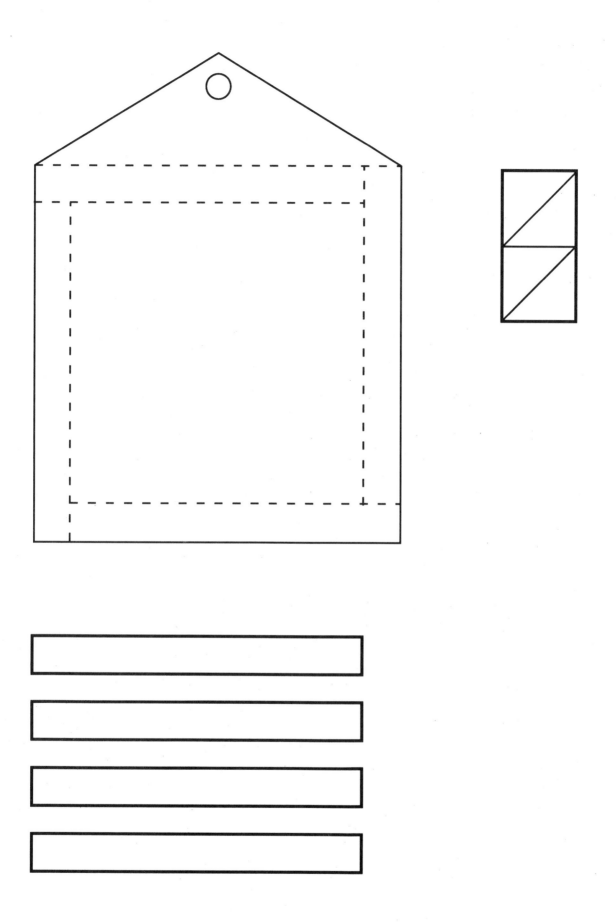

Woven Basket

Technique used:

Paper weaving - frame structure.

Equipment needed:

coloured card   stapler
scissors   felt pens
glue   wax crayons

How to make the example:

Step 1.   Photocopy the sheet opposite onto coloured card or paste onto card, one per child.

Step 2.   Cut out the strips of card and decorate with simple patterns e.g.

     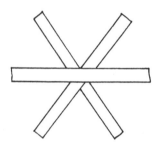

Step 3.   Take three strips of card and glue them together, one on top of the other X to make a simple star shape.

Step 4.   Take one of the longer strips of card and glue the ends together to form a circle.

Step 5.   Glue the ends of the star strips Z to the circle which will form the rim of the basket. Make sure that the decorated sides of the card are facing outwards.

Step 6.   Weave into the basket sides the other two decorated strips, glueing the ends.

Step 7.   Attach the 2 decorated handles marked 'H' and 'G' by stapling them into place as in the diagram at the top of the page.

Step 8.   Photocopy the circle from this page and glue onto card to create the base of the basket. Glue the base inside the basket forming a flat bottom.

How the idea may be developed:

Let the pupils create their own woven baskets using a variety of materials e.g. yarns, strips of fabric, ribbon, decorated papers etc. Increase the size of the basket by lengthening the strips and increasing them in number.

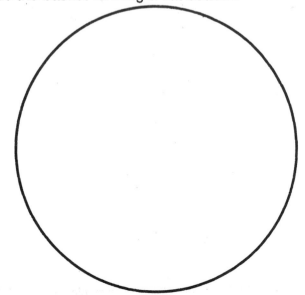

Z Z Z

A B C H G F E D

X X X

Z Z Z

Woven Fabric Wall Hanging

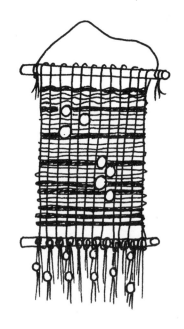

Technique used:
Woven fabrics & frame structures - to show how a fabric can be built up out of yarn. (N.B. Warp threads run lengthways, Weft threads run horizontally in a criss cross manner.)

Equipment needed:

wools	plastic bodkin	beas
dowel	bench hook	yarns
needle	junior hacksaw	glue
cottons	utility snips	string
buttons	sequins	

How to make the example:

Step 1. Photocopy the sheet opposite, one per child.

Step 2. Glue the sheet onto thick card and cut out the loom shape around the solid black lines.

Step 3. From a selection of wools, yarns, cottons and string, let the pupils select the one they wish to use for creating the warp on their loom.

Step 4. Tie one end of the warp thread to the end of the loom marked A and create the warp on the loom as in the diagram pulling the threads tight to make the card loom bow slightly.

Step 5. When the loom has been threaded tie off the warp thread at B.

Step 6. Let the pupils select a length of thread and using a plastic bodkin weave through the warp thread creating the weft.

Step 7. When the end of the warp thread is reached, repeat the process in the opposite direction and carry on until the thread is finished.

Step 8. Tie onto the first piece of thread the second piece. The second piece can be of a different colour, shade or texture depending on the child.

Step 9. Repeat the process until the card loom is covered. Make sure that all the weft threads have been pushed up the warp threads creating a strong structure and tie off the end of the thread to the warp.

Step 10. Cut 2 pieces of dowel 22cms long.

Step 11. Unhook the weaving from the loom and thread one piece of dowel through the loops at the top and the other piece of dowel through the bottom loops.

Step 12. Tie a length of thread to the ends of the top support as in the diagram to make the weaving into a wall hanging.

Step 13. Now Experiment:
Attach braids, plaits, wools etc. to the bottom of the hanging by glueing or sewing. Attach beads, sequins etc. to the hanging itself.

How the idea may be developed:

Looms can be made by attaching lolly sticks with carpet tape to the opposite ends of a shoe box or similar container. Woven fabrics resist stretching (tension) best when pulled either along the warp or the weft thread. The pupils could disassemble a shirt or hat to discover how the shape and strength of the material is created.

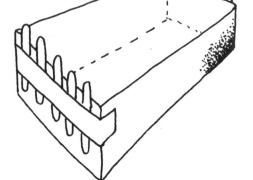

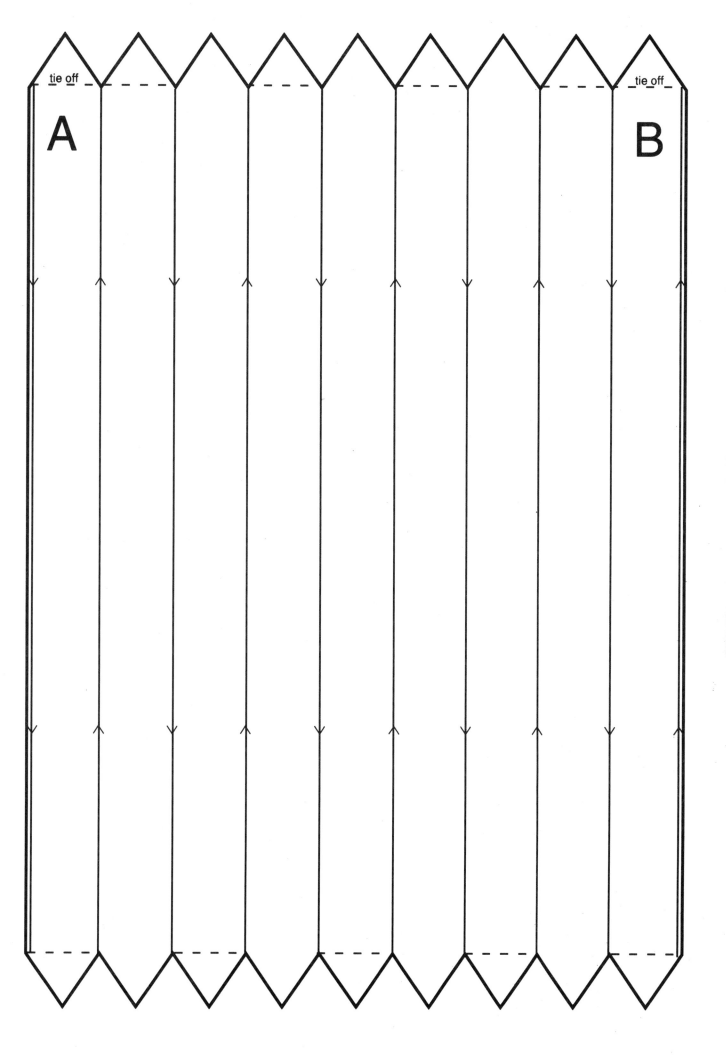

tie off

A

B

tie_off

tie off

tie_off

Chair

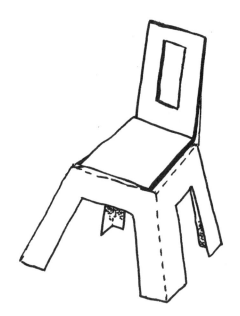

Technique used:
Testing the strength of a paper chair and a card chair of the same design. A chair is good example of a man made structure. The chair has to be strong enough to support its own weight and the weight of a person sitting on it.

Equipment needed:

card	scissors	weights
glue	felt pens	play people

How to make the example:

Step 1. Photocopy the sheet opposite on to card, one per child.

Step 2. Cut out the shapes around the solid black lines.

Step 3. Cut down the 4 short unbroken lines on the chair legs. These will enable the tabs to be folded down to attach the seat of the chair.

Step 4. Cut out the 2 squares from the centre of the chair back. Show the children how to carefully make a hole through the centre of the squares with the pointed end of a pair of scissors and then carefully cut out around the solid black lines. (Take care with pointed scissors!)

Step 5. Fold along the broken lines.

Step 6. Decorate the chair. (If the chair is to be tested to destruction then do not let the pupils decorate it as this would be a waste of their time.)

Step 7. Place glue on tab E and fold under the leg on section A as in the diagram.

Step 8. Fold inwards tabs A,B,C and D.

Step 9. Apply glue to the tabs A,B,C and D and glue to the underside of the seat of the chair.

Step 10. Apply glue to the back of F and glue to the other back section as in the diagram.

Step 11. Glue the legs attached to the back section to the legs on the chair base.

Step 12. Allow the glue to dry and test the chair's strength using play people and / or weights.

Step 13. Repeat the whole process making the chair out of paper.

How the idea may be developed:

Can the children recreate the chair using strip wood or lolly sticks? Let the children try to create a folding chair. Remember the chair must fold up to be carried or put away yet should be stable when someone sits on it. They should investigate an actual deck chair and use construction kits prior to making the chair with construction materials e.g. Briomec, Plastic Meccano. Can the children transfer the knowledge of making stable structures to creating other pieces of furniture e.g. a table, bed, folding step ladders etc.

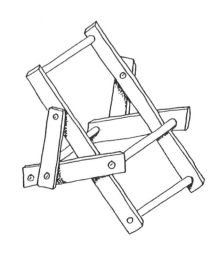

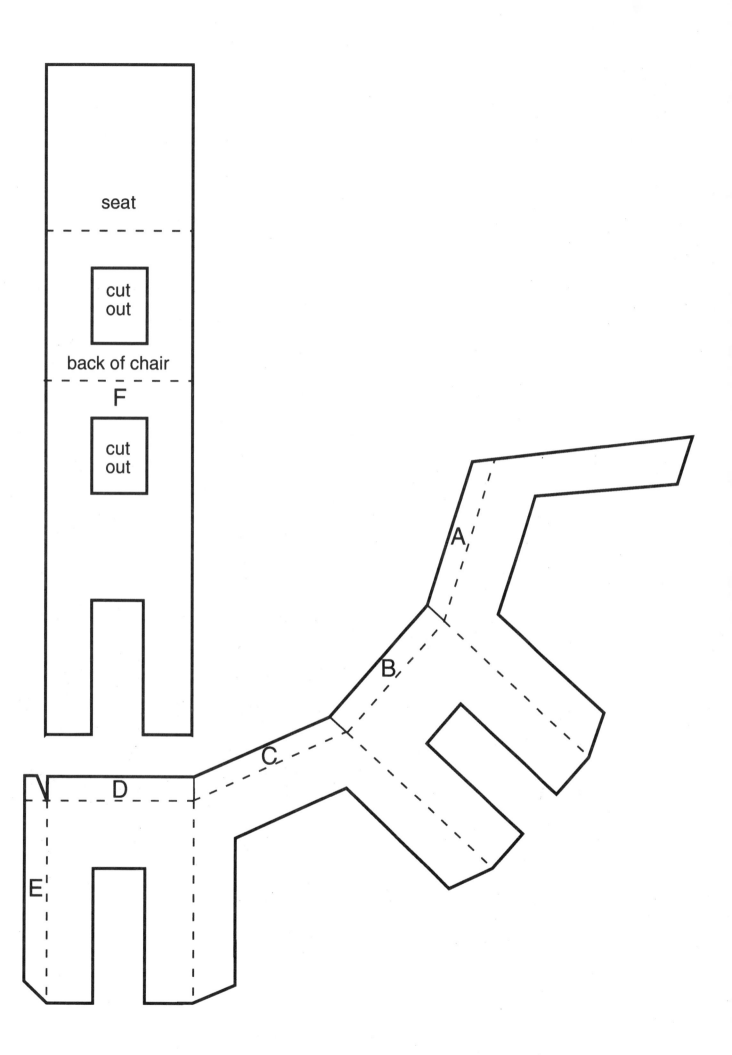

seat

cut out

back of chair

F

cut out

A

B

C

D

E

Lifting Drawbridge

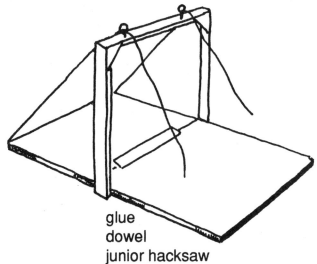

Technique used:

Single leaf opening bridge
using a tape hinge.

Equipment needed:

strip wood	carpet tape	glue
string	bradawl	dowel
thickcard	screw eyes	junior hacksaw
bench hook	triangulated corner strengtheners	

How to make the example:

Step 1. Photocopy the sheet opposite, one per group of children.

Step 2. Cut out the shapes around the solid black lines and use as templates.

Step 3. Stick the lifting section and the fixed section onto thick card and cut the thick card to the shape of the patterns.

Step 4. Place the sides nearest the shaded areas A and C together leaving a very small gap and place a strip of carpet tape from one end to the other creating a hinged joining.

Step 5. Cut 7 pieces of strip wood, each one measuring 10cm in length.

Step 6. Lay 4 of the pieces of strip wood in a square pattern as in the diagram.

Step 7. Glue the triangulated corner strengtheners from the photocopied sheet onto card and cut them out.

Step 8. Glue 4 of the triangulated strengtheners onto the corners of the strip wood as in the diagram.

Step 9. When dry, turn the square over and glue 4 strengtheners on the underside corners.

Step 10. Glue one of the sides of the strengthened square under the shaded area A on the fixed section of the bridge.

Step 11. Glue the 3 remaining pieces of strip wood central ly under the shaded areas B,C and D.

Step 12. Place the photocopied pattern E onto the top section of the frame and mark the positions of the 2 black dots with a bradawl.

Step 13. Screw the 2 eyes (curtain hooks) into the holes made with the bradawl.

Step 14. Cut 2 pieces of string 50cms long.

Step 15. Glue one end of each of the pieces of string under the lifting section B.

Step 16. Thread the other end of each piece of string through the screw eyes in the top section of the frame.

Step 17. By pulling the unattached ends of the 2 pieces of string, the lifting section of the bridge will raise.

How the idea may be developed:

Can the pupils make a double leaf opening bridge? The children can use construction kits such as Briomec, Plastic Meccano and Lasy to create moving bridges of their own. The bridges could slide out from, for example, a river bank or swing from one bank to another.

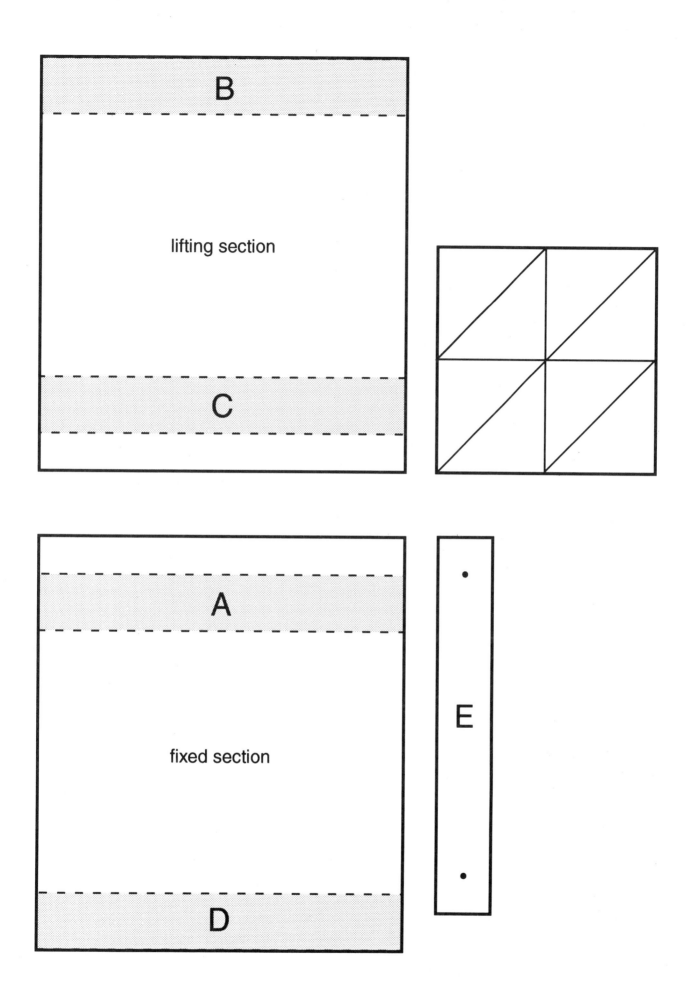

B

lifting section

C

A

fixed section

D

E

Wind Powered Dodgems

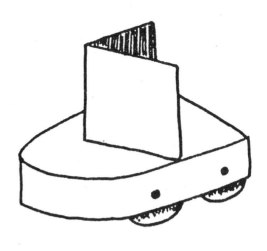

Technique used:

Holes for free moving axles.

Equipment needed:

5mm dowel
junior hacksaw   coloured crayons
bench hook   felt pens
3mm card wheels   single hole punch
hairdryer   vice
glue

How to make the example:

Step 1. Photocopy the sheet opposite onto card or paste onto card, one per child.
Step 2. Cut out the pieces along the solid black lines.
Step 3. Cut 2 pieces of dowel equal in length to the 2 templates for axles from the photocopied sheet.
Step 4. Decorate the sides, base and sail for the dodgem.
Step 5. Fold the side plates along the broken lines and cut down the short black lines forming tabs to allow the base of the dodgem to be attached.
Step 6. Apply glue to the small folded sections of the side plates and attach to the base as in the diagram.
Step 7. Fold the sail in half along the broken line.
Step 8. Fold along the broken line at the base of the sail to create tabs to which glue is applied.
Step 9. Glue the sail to the base on the shaded area.
Step 10. Punch 4 holes through the black dots on the side plates.
Step 11. Push the axles through the holes on one side of the dodgem.
Step 12. Place the wheels on the axles. Wheels should be a tight fit.
Step 13. Push the axles through the holes on the opposite side of the dodgem and position the wheels near the sides of the dodgem.
Step 14. Test the dodgems by blowing them behind the sails using a hairdryer.

How the idea may be developed:

Create a variety of lightweight plank chassis and add sails to create land yachts. The axle holders can be clip pegs, felt pen barrels or paper clips. For detailed instructions read "Design and Make Moving Toys and Models" published by Topical Resources.

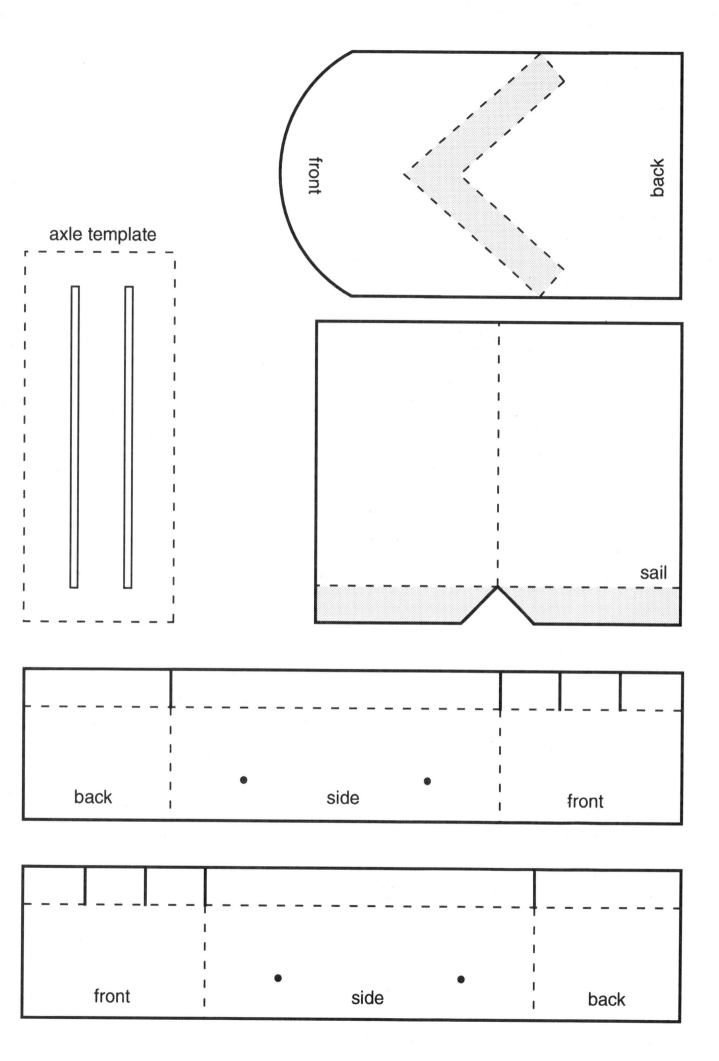

axle template

front

back

sail

back   side   front

front   side   back

Tin Can Roundabout

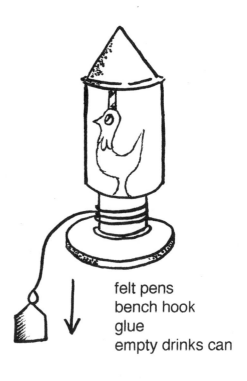

Technique used:

Rotational motion - round and round
movement powered by a falling weight.

Equipment needed:

junior hacksaw	string
weight	cotton reel
5mm dowel	card
sticky tape	low melt glue gun
large wooden wheel with 4mm hole	

felt pens
bench hook
glue
empty drinks can

How to make the example:

Step 1. Photocopy the sheet opposite onto card or paste onto card, one per child.
Step 2. Cut out the pieces around the solid black lines.
Step 3. Decorate the pieces using felt pens or pencil crayons.
Step 4. Glue the tab on the decorated roundabout to the side of an empty drinks can and wrap around the can securing in place with glue or sticky tape.
Step 5. Glue the circles to the top and base of the drinks can using a low melt glue gun - a trained adult should do this for the children.
Step 6. Apply glue to the shaded area on the cone pattern and attach to the underside of 'A' creating a cone.
Step 7. Glue the cone onto the top of the roundabout.
Step 8. Cut a piece of dowel 4cm long and push one end into the centre hole of a large wooden wheel. The dowel must be a tight fit.
Step 9. Using a low melt glue gun, attach a cotton reel to the centre of the base of the roundabout as in the diagram.
Step 10. Using sticky tape attach one end of a 50cm length of string to the cotton reel.
Step 11. Tie a light weight or a pice of plasticene to the other end of the piece of string
Step 12. Wrap the string tightly around the cotton reel and hold in place.
Step 13. Position the base of the roundabout near the edge of a table and hold down the base so that the ride will not fall over. Release the weight and as it free falls, watch the ride spin.

How the idea may be developed:

Let the children vary the weight used to test their models. Do lighter / heavier weights affect the performance of the roundabout? Let the pupils investigate objects that spin e.g. spinning tops, roulette wheels, turn tables, spinners. Can the pupils make simple roundabouts using construction kits? Which ones are suitable? Try Lasy or First Gear or similar construction kits. Discuss how the models can be powered and test e.g. finger power, hand power, rubber band powered etc.

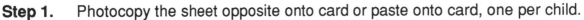

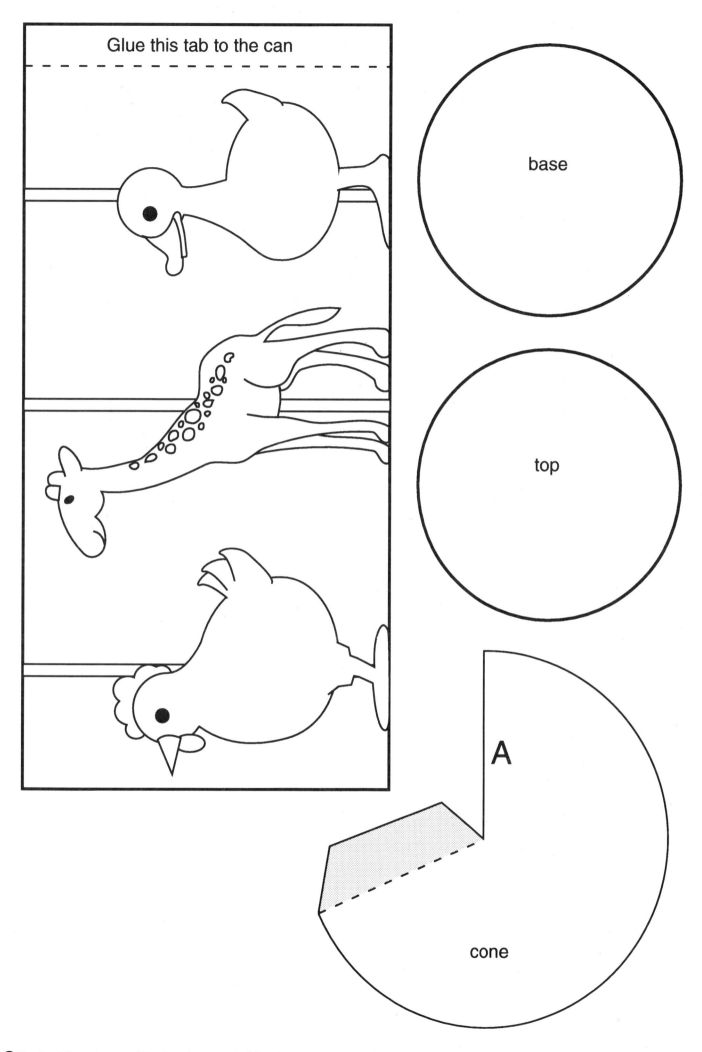

Glue this tab to the can

base

top

A

cone

Slide

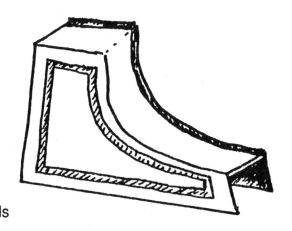

Technique used:

Linear motion - straight line motion.

Equipment needed:

scissors   marble
glue   coloured pencils
felt pens

How to make the example:

Step 1. Photocopy the sheet opposite onto card or paste onto card, one per child or group of children.

Step 2. Cut out the pieces carefully along the solid black lines.

Step 3. Fold along the broken lines between A-B, C-D, E-F and G-H.

Step 4. Decorate the pieces using felt pens or pencil crayons.

Step 5. Take the strip of card that will form the slide and cut along the short unbroken lines along both sides.

Step 6. Apply glue to the folded tabs on the edge of the line markd A-B.

Step 7. Glue 'A' to the edge of 'E' as in the drawing at the top of the pagel.

Step 8. Continue glueing the slide and the side panel together following the line marked so that there is a side created to the slide. **N.B. the slide should be set below the top edge of the side panels.**

Step 9. Repeat steps 6 to 8 with the other side of the slide and the right hand side panel.

Step 10. Place glue along the panel marked 'X' at the back of the slide and attach the other back panel over the top of it.

Step 11. Test the slide using a marble or a ball of plasticene.

How the idea may be developed:

Once a paper prototype has been made then the children can experiment with other materials e.g. card, reclaimed materials, lolly sticks, corrugated plastic and card. Experiment using the above technique to create a longer slide with an undulating surface. Can the pupils make a slide using the large P.E. apparatus? Test materials to find the best surface for a slide. Try - card, tin foil, sand paper. Does the slope of the slide affect the performance? Can the pupils create a wider range of slides e.g. water slides or chutes?

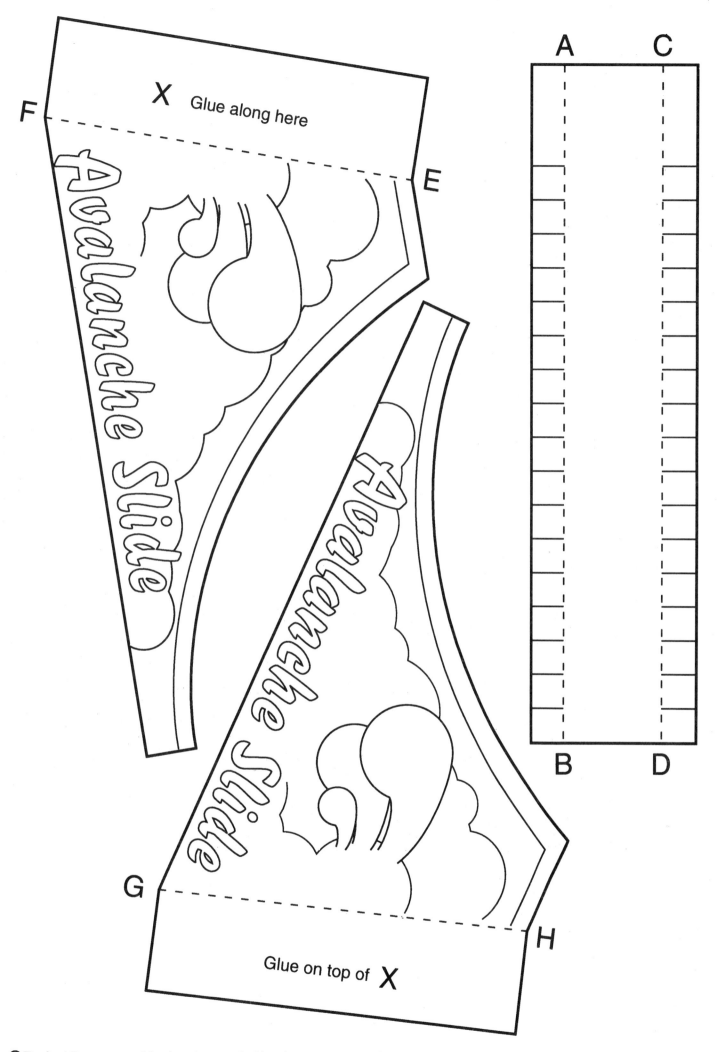

F

X Glue along here

E

Avalanche Slide

A C

B D

Avalanche Slide

G

H

Glue on top of X

Helter Skelter

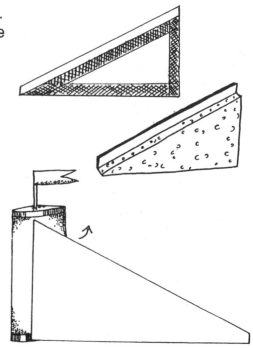

Technique used:

Inclines wrapped around a cylinder
(e.g. a screw)

Equipment needed:

scissors	2 cm thick sponge	low melt glue gun
card	glue	marble / bead
felt pens	paints	card cylinder -10cm in length
5mm dowel	double sided tape	5cm diameter wheels

How to make the example:

Step 1. Photocopy the sheet opposite, one per child or group of children.

Step 2. Cut out the shapes around the solid black lines and use as templates.

Step 3. Draw around the sponge template onto sponge which is about 2cm thick and cut the sponge to shape.

Step 4. Draw around the card template onto 4 sheet thickness card and cut the card to shape.

Step 5. Decorate the reverse side of the card triangle using Fairground Art.

Step 6. Stick the sponge to the shaded area of the card.

Step 7. Glue a wheel onto the top of the cylinder and a wheel to the bottom.

Step 8. Cut a piece of dowel 5cm in length

Step 9. Decorate the flag photocopy and glue to one end of the dowel by applying glue to the shaded area and wrapping it around the dowel.

Step 10. Push the dowel into the centre hole of the wheel on the top of the cylinder.

Step 11. Place double sided tape around the 3 sides of the sponge as in the diagram.

Step 12. Fasten the shortest side of the sponge vertically to the cylinder as in the diagram.

Step 13. Wrap the sponge tightly around the cylinder.

Step 14. Test the Helter Skelter using a small marble or a bead.

How the idea may be developed:

The pupils can examine and investigate screws and drill bits as these are pieces of equipment that use inclines.

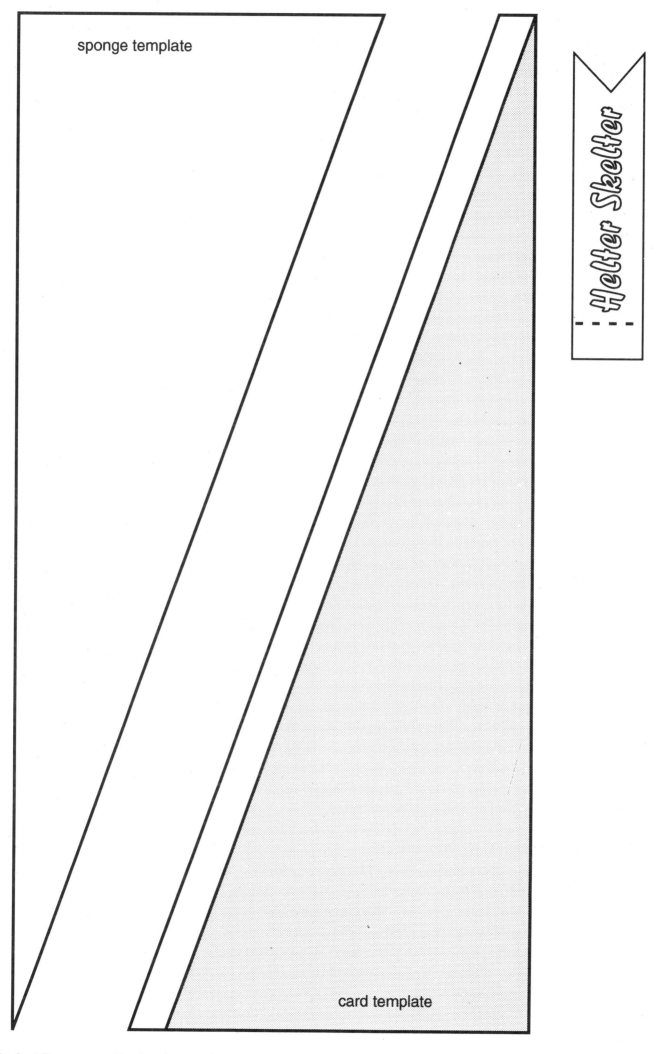

sponge template

card template

Helter Skelter

Paper Carrier Bag

Let the pupils investigate and disassemble some manufactured paper bags, carriers and cartons before this activity takes place to show them how the structures can be made.

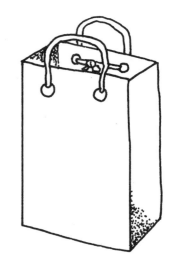

Technique used:

Manufactured shell structure

Equipment needed:

felt pens	single hole punch	
coloured pencils	cord	
scissors	glue	ribbon

How to make the example:

Step 1. Photocopy the sheet opposite, one per child.
Step 2. Cut around the soild black lines.
Step 3. Let the pupils decorate the reverse side of the photocopy using pencil crayons and felt pens. A selection of manufactured paper bags and wrapping papers can be collected and shown to the pupils to let them see the variety of designs and decorations.
Step 4. The pupils should be shown how to use a single hole punch or a paper drill and make 4 holes in the position of the circles on the bag.
Step 5. The pupils will need help in folding along the broken lines.
Step 6. Apply glue to 'C' and glue over the tab as directed forming an open ended cuboid.
Step 7. Apply glue to 'D' and 'E' and fold to create the gusset at the base of the carrier bag. The pupils will need help with this. Glue down the triangular flaps.
Step 8. Cut 2 pieces of cord or ribbon 20cm long - these will form the handles.
Step 9. Push each end of one handle through the holes on one side of the bag and tie securely with a knot on the inside of the bag.
Step 10. Repeat with the other handle.
Step 11. Test the strength of the bag with weights. If however the bag is to be tested to destruction, do not let the pupils decorate the test article as this would be a waste of their time.

How the idea may be developed:

The photocopy could be pasted onto thicker paper to create a stronger structure, one that would withstand more weight. Could card be pasted behind the hole positions and holes punched through the paper and card to create strengthened holes for the handles? The photocopy can be enlarged to A3 size to make a larger paper carrier bag. Does size affest the strength of the carrier? The children could decorate the bag with a particular theme to create a carrier for a Birthday present or Easter Egg etc..

Glue along here

C

E

Apply glue here

B

Stick the glued tabs under here

A

D

Apply glue here

Stick the glued tab under here

Tools and Techniques

The techniques needed to create the structures and fairground rides can be taught to groups of children or individuals depending on their age and previous experience. The teacher will need to know the children's experience level in the following skills and techniques and practice if necessary: Measuring and marking, cutting and shaping, finishing, joining and combining.

Measuring and Marking

Are the children capable of measuring accurately using standard measurements? If the children are not ready for using centimetres, then templates can be provided for them to use to mark the cutting position. Do the children know how to make a paper pattern or template? Using the photocopied sheets will give the children valuable practice in using manufactured patterns, nets and templates prior to them creating their own.

Cutting and Shaping

The children should be taught how to use cutting tools correctly and safely to ensure quality products created in a safe environment.

Scissors

A variety of scissors should be provided within the school: Right and left handed, round and pointed ended, large and small.

Safety Snips

A useful tool for cutting a variety of reclaimed materials and thick card.

Junior Hacksaw

Strong pistol grip hacksaws are safe to use and blades are easily changed.

Drill

A pistol grip drill is easy to use and drill bits on most models can be stored in the handles.

Utility Snips

These are scissor action and will cut heavy cardboard, thin metal and corrugated plastic.

Circle Cutter

Protect table tops and floors when using this piece of equipment as it contains a sharp blade. Out of thick card or plastic it will cut a circle of up to 35cm in diameter.

Round File

A useful pice of equipment for increasing the size of holes and for smoothing drilled holes and sharp edges.

Craft Knife

Only use knives with retractable blades. Use in conjunction with a cutting mat and local safety regulations.

Metal Safety Ruler

An essential piece of equipment if craft knives are to be used as it keeps the pupils fingers out of the way!

Vice

Young children should hold their material for cutting or drilling in a vice to avoid slipping.

Tools and Techniques

Joining and Combining
The pupils should be taught the correct type of glue to use for a particular job and also the correct joinings that will allow movement, create a stable structure etc..

Brass Fasteners
Simple brass fasteners can be used to create a joining that allows movement. The pupils should be shown how to create a hole using the pointed end of a pair of scissors [take care!] or pencil point pushed through the material and into a ball of plasticene.

Low melt Glue Gun
These operate at a lower temperature than the traditional hot glue gun and yet the glue can burn the skin.Protective gloves can be worn when using the gun which should only be used under close supervision. It forms a secure bond when used to join wood and plastic.

Loose and Tight Fit Dowel
Ready drilled wheels with a 4mm hole are a tight fit on 5mm dowel. If however you require the dowel to be free moving then the hole in the centre of a wheel can be redrilled by using a drill fitted with a 6mm drill bit.

Strip and Dowel Construction
A versatile technique that forms a rigid structure without the use of adhesives.

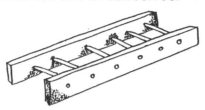

Card Triangles
Square section and strip wood can be fastened at 90˚ angles by using card triangles glued to the top and bottom surfaces of the wood. These form a suprisingly strong structure that is useful for creating a frame.

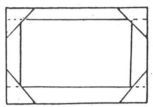

Finishings
The mixing and application of various paints, stains, varnishes and collage materials should be investigated to discover the different effects that can be achieved. The pupils need to experiment with a wide range of mediums e.g. felt pens, coloured pencils, paint, pastels etc..Children should question which ones are the most suitable for detailed work.

Pupils should be taught how to clad structures in card and paper to conceal frameworks and add texture by using a mixture of paint and glue with a variety of additives e,g sand, sawdust. Reclaimed boxes used in the construction of models should be turned inside out to enable a quality finish to be achieved and if stickty tape is used, remember that masking tape and brown tape can be painted whereas sellotape is almost impossible to hide. Models and structures should look attractive as well as work efficiently.

Tower

Technique used:

Cross Bracing

Equipment needed:

brass fasteners   thick card
sticky tape   hole punch
scissors

How to make the example:

Step 1.   Divide the class of children into working groups of 4.
Step 2.   Photocopy the sheet opposite, one per child.
Step 3.   Cut out the pieces around the solid black lines and glue onto thick card -crisp boxes are a good source of thick reclaimed card. Cut the card to the size of the photocopied pieces.
Step 4.   Punch holes through the centres of the black dots.

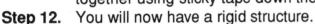

Step 5.   Take the 4 strips marked A and using brass fasteners attach to the side strips as in the diagram.
Step 6.   Test the strength of the structure. What do the children discover?
Step 7.   The structure is unstable. Let the 4 children in their working groups discuss why the structure is unstable.
Step 8.   Take the 4 strips marked B and attach them to the structure using brass fasteners as in the diagram.
Step 9.   Test the strength of the structure again.
Step 10. To strengthen the structure further, add one of the strips marked C across the 2 top holes in the side strips and the other strip marked C across the bottom 2 holes in the side strips.
Step 11. All 4 children in the working party must now combine their strengthened side panels together to form a tower. Lay the 4 pieces side by side as in the diagram and fasten together using sticky tape down the edges.

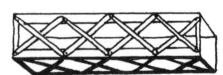

Step 12. You will now have a rigid structure.

How the idea may be developed:
Can the children create a taller tower using more cross bracings and longer side strips? Does the tower become less stable the higher it is made? If so, why? (As towers become taller, the increased force from the weight of materials places stress on the lower parts of the structure, this can cause the tower to collapse. When the centre of gravity of the tower swings outside the base, or when the downward force from the materials causes one of the lower sections to slip, then the structure collapses.)

A
A
A
A

B
B
B
B

C
C

side strip

side strip

Crane

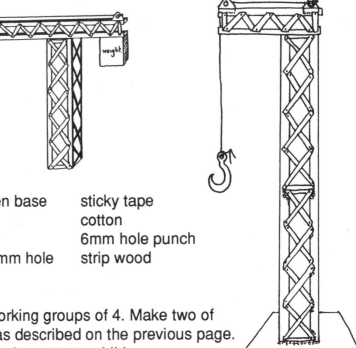

Technique used:
Cross bracing and simple
pulley winding mechanism.

Equipment needed:

pva glue	20cm square wooden base	sticky tape
scissors	brass fasteners	cotton
thick card	low melt glue gun	6mm hole punch
5mm dowel	small wheels with 4mm hole	strip wood

How to make the example:

Step 1. Divide the children into working groups of 4. Make two of the cross braced towers as described on the previous page.

Step 2. Photocopy the sheet opposite, one per child.

Step 3. Glue the 4 sheets per group onto thick card and cut out the pieces.

Step 4. Fold the pieces marked A along the broken lines and glue the pieces to the two tops and two bottoms of the cross braced towers.

Step 5. When dry, glue the two towers together as in the diagram.

Step 6. Using the low melt glue gun, attach the tower to the middle of a wooden base Caution! Glue guns are hot enough to burn flesh, care must be taken and if possible protective gloves should be worn.

Step 7. Use one of the top side panels (D) and one of the bottom side panels (E) to create one side of the crane arm. Punch holes through the black dots.

Step 8. Take 6 of the strips marked B and attach to the border strips as in the diagram. The children should decide where the holes are to be placed on the strips marked B.

Step 9. Attach the strips marked C to the end holes on the top and bottom strips.

Step 10. Repeat steps 7, 8 and 9 to create the other side of the crane arm.

Step 11. To make the top, cut 8 pieces of strip wood that each measure 6cm in length.

Step 12. To join the two sides of the arm, glue the 8 pieces on the inside of one of the crane arms, 4 equally spaced on the bottom strip and 4 equally placed on the top strip. Glue the other ends of the strip wood to the other crane arm.

Step 13. Cut out the 4 triangles and shaded areas from the thick card and punch holes through the black dots. These holes must be 6mm in size to allow free movement of the dowel. Glue the shaded areas of the axle holders to the 4 corners of the crane arm.

Step 14. Cut 2 pieces of dowel that measure 10cms in length and push them through the holes in the axle holders.

Step 15. Place wooden wheels onto the ends of the dowel to keep the pieces in place.

Step 16. Cut a piece of cotton 80cm in length and tape one end to the axle dowel at the right hand side of the frame. Tie the hook onto the other end and place the cotton over the left hand axle. Weight the hook with plasticine.

Step 17. Glue the arm to the top of the tower.

Step 18. Turn the wheels on the right hand side and the hook will raise and lower the load.

How the idea may be developed:
Can the pupils develop a catch to hold the raised load in place? The crane arm can be made longer but would need a counter balance to make it stable as in the diagram.

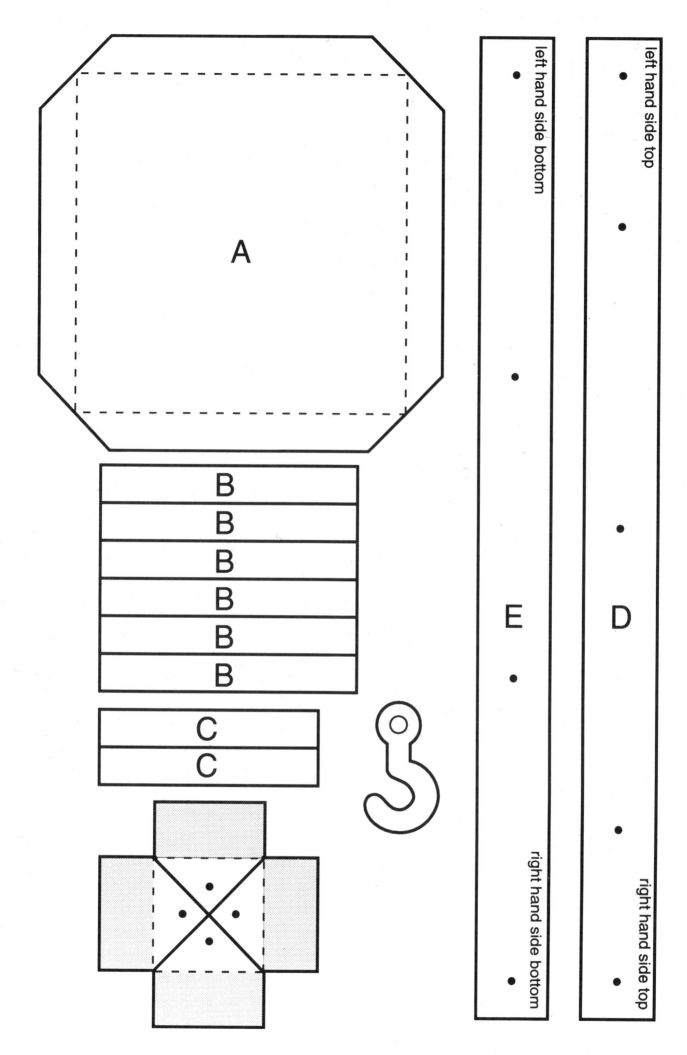

Pylon

Technique used:

Frame structures.

Equipment needed:

    artstraws
    masking tape
    pipe cleaners
    weights

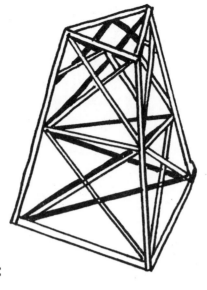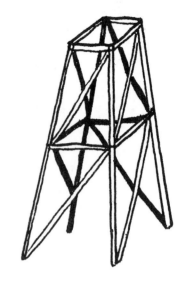

How to make the example:

Step 1.   Photocopy the sheet opposite, one per child or group of children.

Step 2.   Each child or group of children must select a tower that they wish to make. Each working party should be given an equal number of artstraws (e.g. 36) pipecleaners (e.g. 5) and an equal length of masking tape (e.g. 1 metre) Wrap the measured length of masking tape around a pencil to enable the tape to be used efficiently.

Step 3.   Create the chosen tower design using the materials given. Stress the importance of using all the given materials to make the testing fair.

Step 4.   Test the strength of the finished towers using weights.

Step 5.   Record the results in some form. The pupils should create their own recording system.

Step 6.   Discuss which tower is the strongest and why.

Forces   Two forces act on and in structures - compression and tension. Compression is a pushing force. Tension is a pulling force.

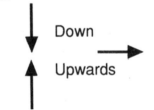

Compression from weight   Down   These forces acting together cause the legs to buckle when they are being compressed.

Compression from base   Upwards

The horizontal cross members of some of the towers / pylons are under tension. The legs are trying to bow outwards because of the compression and the cross section is pulled equally outwards at each end, it is therefore under tension. Providing the forces balance each other, the structure will remain stable. Collapse occurs when the forces are no longer balanced.

How the idea may be developed:

Can the children make a tall tower or pylon that has a lift? Do they have the knowledge of the workings of a pulley system? The lift mechanism can be a simple wind up mechanism as in the diagram. Remember! For the lift to work it will need a clear run up and down the centre or outside of the tower / pylon.

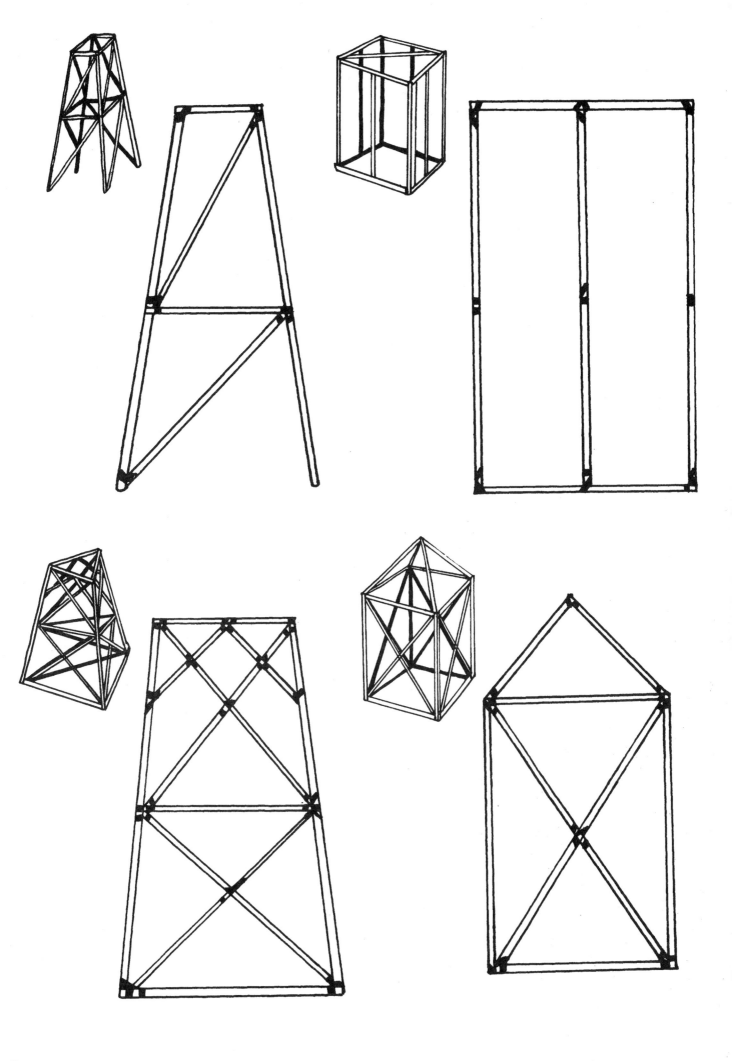

Box Container

Technique used:

Frame structure with shell covering.
Frames and Structures can be made using 10cm
square section wood and card triangle corner
strengtheners. Using this method, you can design
and make almost any kind of structure.

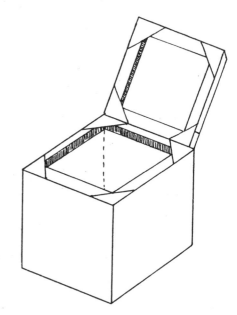

Equipment needed:

10mm square section wood   pva glue
junior hacksaw   bench hook
                                  card

How to make the example:

Step 1. Cut 12 pieces of 10mm square section wood measuring 9cm in length.

Step 2. Lay the pieces on a flat surface forming
three squares as in the diagram.
Each side will measure 10cm in length.

Step 3. The structures are weak, they are not rigid.
The corners need strengthening to create rigid structures.

Step 4. Photocopy the sheet opposite onto card or paste onto thin card one per child.

Step 5. Cut out the shape A from the photocopied sheet and then cut out the
triangles from the shape.

Step 6. Using a small amount of pva glue,
attach 4 triangles to the corners of
each of the squares as in the diagram.

Step 7. When dry, turn the squares over and glue triangles on the corners of the
underside. When the glue is dry, the squares will be rigid, strengthened by
the triangles placed on the corners.

Step 8. Cut out the shape B from the photocopied sheet and cut out the 8 squares
marked within it. Fold along the diagonal broken lines and cut along the solid
black line.

Step 9. Slide the triangle marked C under
triangle D and glue into place
forming a 3D corner strengthener
as in the diagram.

Step 10. Cut 4 pieces of 10mm square section wood measuring 8cm in length.

Step 11. Place glue into 4 of the corner strengtheners and position at the corners of
one of the squares, sitting a piece of the 8cm long wood at right angles.

Step 12. Place one of the remaining squares on top of the uprights and fasten in place
with the 4 remaining 3D corner strengtheners. Allow to dry.

Step 13. Copy the box covering template onto card or photocopy the net increasing
the size from B5 to A4 making the sides measure 10cm in size. (Alterna
tively, use reclaimed card to panel in the sides of the wooden frame.)

Step 14. Cut out the box covering from thin card and fold along the broken lines. Glue
the remaining wooden square onto the lid of the net and glue the
covering around the built 3D frame. Cover any gaps with masking tape.

How the idea may be developed:

The children can now create their own box of any size using this technique. A fastening
can be made for the box using ribbons, velcro etc. and the card decorated prior to
covering the frame.

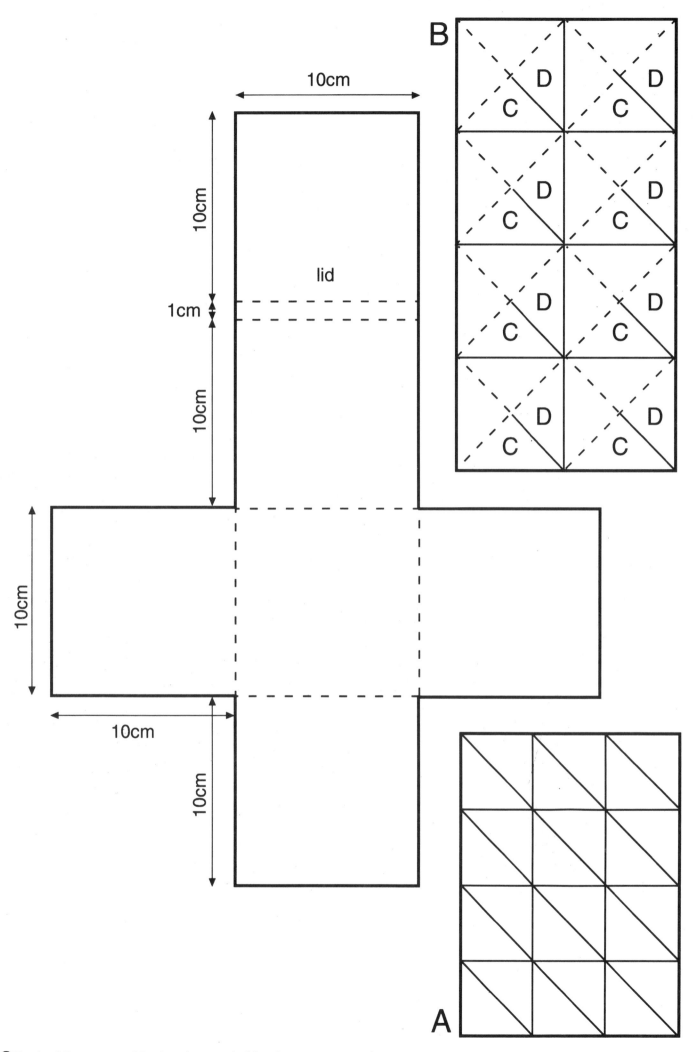

10cm

10cm

lid

1cm

10cm

10cm

10cm

10cm

B

D D

C C

D D

C C

D D

C C

D D

C C

A

A Model House

Technique used:

Frame and shell structure using card triangle strengtheners and card net.

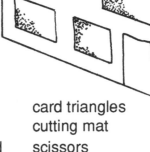

Equipment needed:

card	junior hacksaw	
craft knife	safety ruler	card triangles
felt pens	coloured crayons	cutting mat
pva glue	10mm square section wood	scissors

How to make the example:

Step 1. Cut 4 pieces of 10mm square section wood that measure 19cm in length and 4 pieces that measure 13cm.

Step 2. Use the pieces of wood to create two rectangles as in the diagram.

Step 3. Using the corner strengthening technique from the previous page, glue triangles to both sides of the rectangles as in the diagram.

Step 4. Cut 4 uprights that measure 12cm in length and combine the uprights, the 2 rectangles and eight 3D corner strengtheners (see previous page) to create a cuboid. Remember that because of the width of the wooden frame, the cuboid will measure 14cm x 14cm x 20cm.

Step 5. Photocopy the sheet opposite, one per child and transfer the measurements of the roof net onto 1cm graph paper and cut out. (Alternatively, enlarge the shape 200% on a photocopier.)

Step 6. Glue the full size net to card. Cut out and make up the roof shape.

Step 7. Glue the roof onto the wooden frame.

Step 8. Cover the cuboid frame with card sides.

Step 9. Cut doors and windows as appropriate.

Step 10. Colour with paints or felt tipped pens.

How the idea may be developed:

A model of a Tudor House can be created by making 2 cuboid structures covered with nets, one larger than the other. The larger of the 2 is placed on top as in the diagram and the roofing net can be covered in straw to give an added feeling of authenticity.

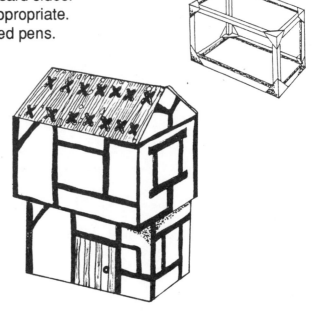

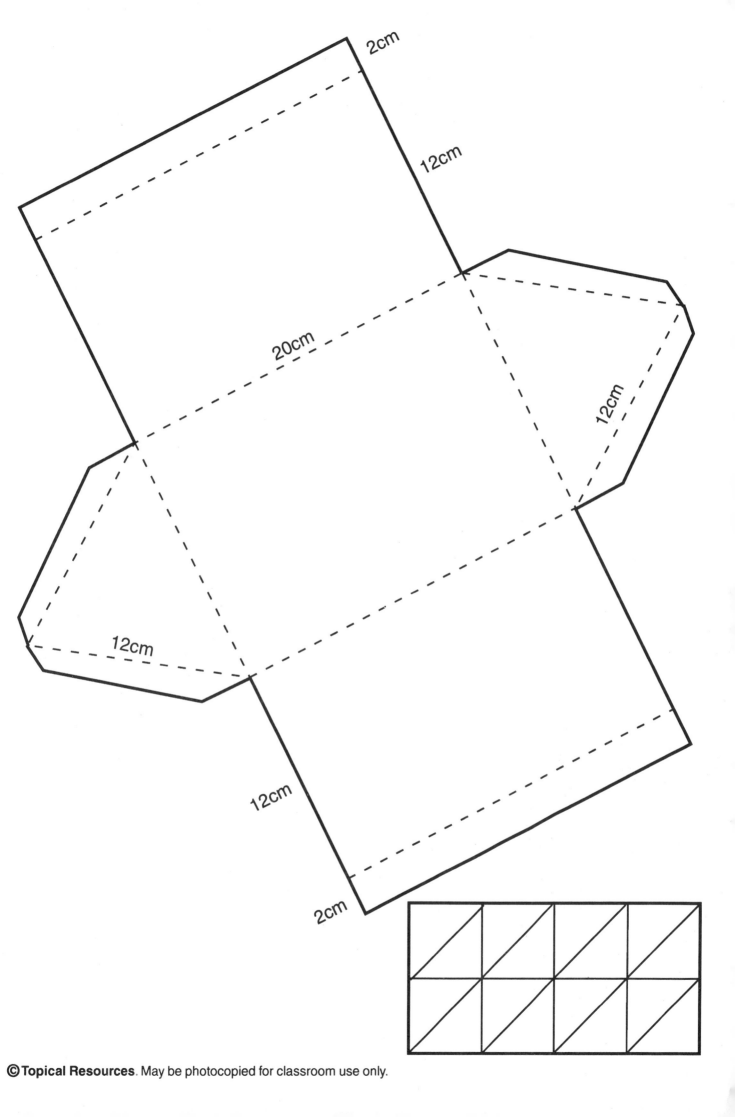

2cm

12cm

20cm

12cm

12cm

12cm

2cm

Supporting Structure

Technique used:

Triangulated frame.

Equipment needed:

glue
bench hook
scissors
strip wood
thick card

junior hacksaw
20cm square base
low melt glue gun
felt pens
coloured pens

How to make the example:

Step 1. Photocopy the sheet opposite, one per child or group of children.
Step 2. Cut out the shapes around the solid black lines and use as templates.
Step 3. Place the side frame A onto thick card, draw around it twice and cut out two side frames.
Step 4. Decorate the frames with fairground art.
Step 5. Cut a piece of strip wood the same length as C which is 14cm in length and using a low melt glue gun, glue the piece of stripwood between the two top edges of the support structures.
Step 6. Use B as a template and cut 2 base strengtheners from thick card.
Step 7. Fold the 2 base strengtheners along the broken lines and glue the tabs to the shaded areas on the side frames as in the diagram.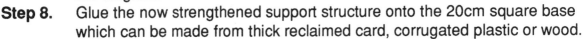
Step 8. Glue the now strengthened support structure onto the 20cm square base which can be made from thick reclaimed card, corrugated plastic or wood.

How the idea may be developed:

This structure can be used to support swings made from a variety of materials.
Let the pupils make observational drawings of triangular frames and structures in their environment.
Can a stronger structure be made by adding an extra frame to the centre of the structure?

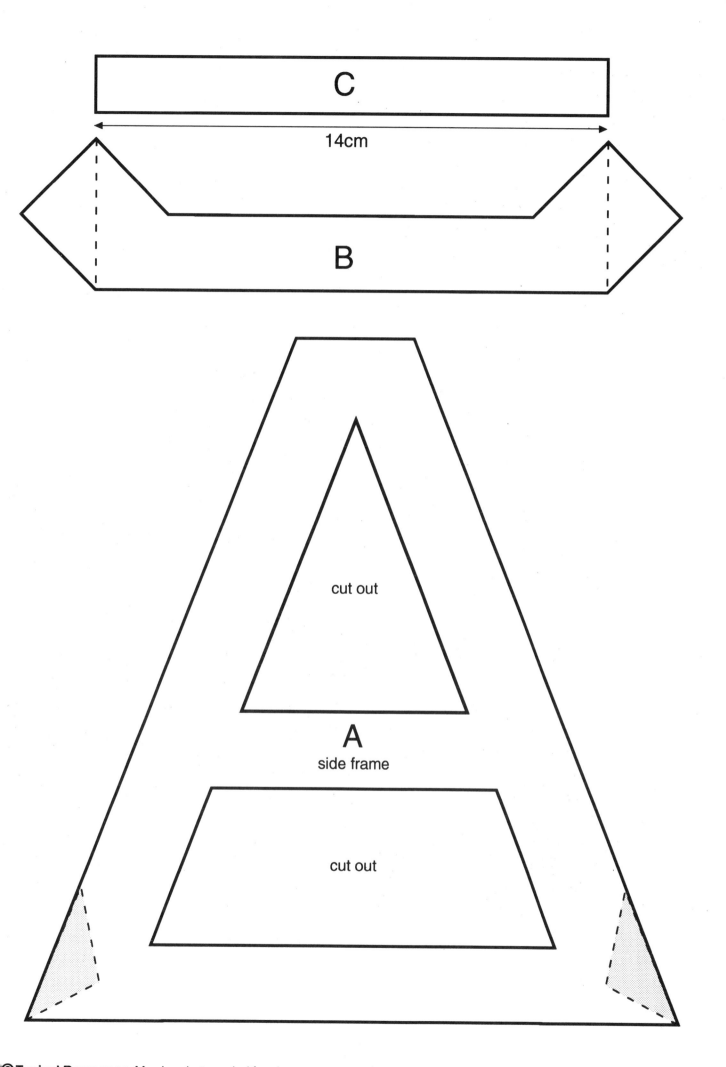

C

14cm

B

A

side frame

cut out

cut out

Swingboats

Technique used:

Oscillatory motion - swinging motion.

Equipment needed:

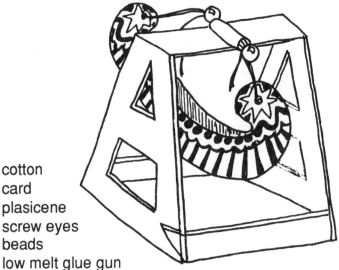

strip wood	cotton
bench hook	card
felt pens	plasicene
coloured crayons	screw eyes
junior haclksaw	beads
drill with 4mm bit	low melt glue gun

How to make the example:

Step 1. Create the structure on the previous page.

Step 2. Photocopy the sheet opposite onto card, one per child or group of children.

Step 3. Cut out the shapes along the solid black lines.

Step 4. Decorate the swingboat shape B using ideas from Fairground Art.

Step 5. Fold along the broken lines on B and fold up the sides of the swingboat.

Step 6. Punch holes through the black dots on the front and back sections of the swingboat.

Step 7. Glue the front and back sections of the boat together in the positions marked 'X'.

Step 8. Glue A onto thick card and glue into the base of the swingboat.

Step 9. Cut 2 pieces of cotton or thin string about 40cm in length.

Step 10 Place a bead in the centre of each piece of cotton and knot in place as in the diagram. It is important that the bead is between one and two centimetres in diameter.

Step 11. Glue a piece of felt pen barrel or artstraw horizontally across the central stripwood section of the structure as in the diagram.

Step 12. Thread the end of one of the pieces of cotton through the pen barrel from front to back and the other piece of thread should be threaded through the barrel from back to front. The beads should be large enough to stop the thread slipping through the barrel.

Step 13. Tie the ends of the threads without the beads, through the holes punched in the front and rear sections of the swingboat.

Step 14. Place plasticene or play people into the swingboat.

Let the pupils make observational drawings of swings on a visit to a playground prior to them creating their own swingboat models.

Can they make the swings:　Swing as high as possible?

　　　　　　　　　　　　　Swing as slowly as possible?

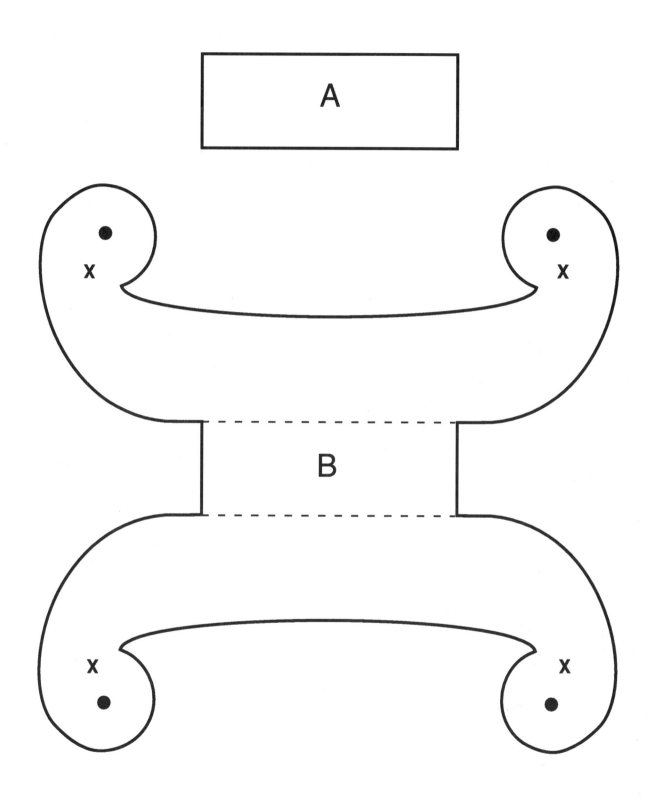

Death Plank

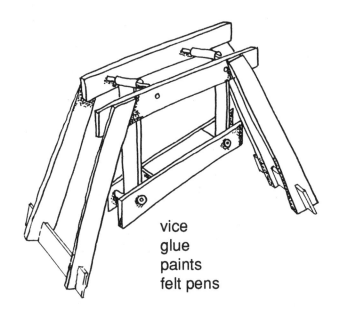

Technique used:

Reciprocatory motion -
back and forth movement.

Equipment needed:

reclaimed thick card	5mm dowel	vice
hole punch	utility snips	glue
junior hacksaw	paper drill	paints
lolly sticks	bench hook	felt pens
sticky tape	artstraws	

How to make the example:

Step 1.   Photocopy the sheet opposite and paste onto thick card, one per group of children.

Step 2.   Cut out the shapes carefully around the solid black lines using utility snips.

Step 3.   Punch holes through the black dots on 'A' and 'D' using a single hole punch or a paper drill.

Step 4.   Glue the 4 strips marked 'B' onto the 2 cross strips marked 'A' as in the diagram below. Place the shaded areas on 'B' onto the shaded areas on 'A'.

Step 5.   Cut 4 pieces of artstraws 2cms in length and fasten with sticky tape across the top and bottom of the strips marked 'C' as in the diagram.

Step 6.   Cut 2 pieces of dowel that measure 6cm in length.

Step 7.   Place the pieces of dowel through the artstraws on the the top of the strip marked 'C'. Ensure that the dowel is free moving in the channel of the artstraws.

Step 8.   Glue the ends of the dowel into the holes on 'A'. one end of one piece into 'A1' on the left hand side and 'A1' on the right hand side and the other piece into 'A2' on the left hand side and 'A2' on the right side.

Step 9.   The structure is not stable. Cut slots in shape E and the feet of all B shapes. Slot E into the feet of B as in the diagram at the top of the page.

Step 10.   Cut 2 pieces of dowel that measure 4cm in length.

Step 11.   Push the 2 pieces of dowel through the artstraws at the end of the strips marked 'C'.

Step 12.   Glue the ends of the dowel into the holes on the strips marked 'D'.

Step 13.   Test the Death plank and decorate.

How the idea may be developed:

Can the pupils make a similar ride using construction kits? Which ones would be suitable for this activity?
Try : Meccano, Duplo, BrioMec, Lasy.
Create a top for the ride so that play people can be placed on it. Experiment with plasticene and string to observe swinging motion.

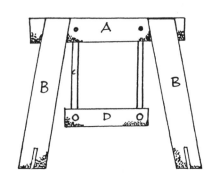

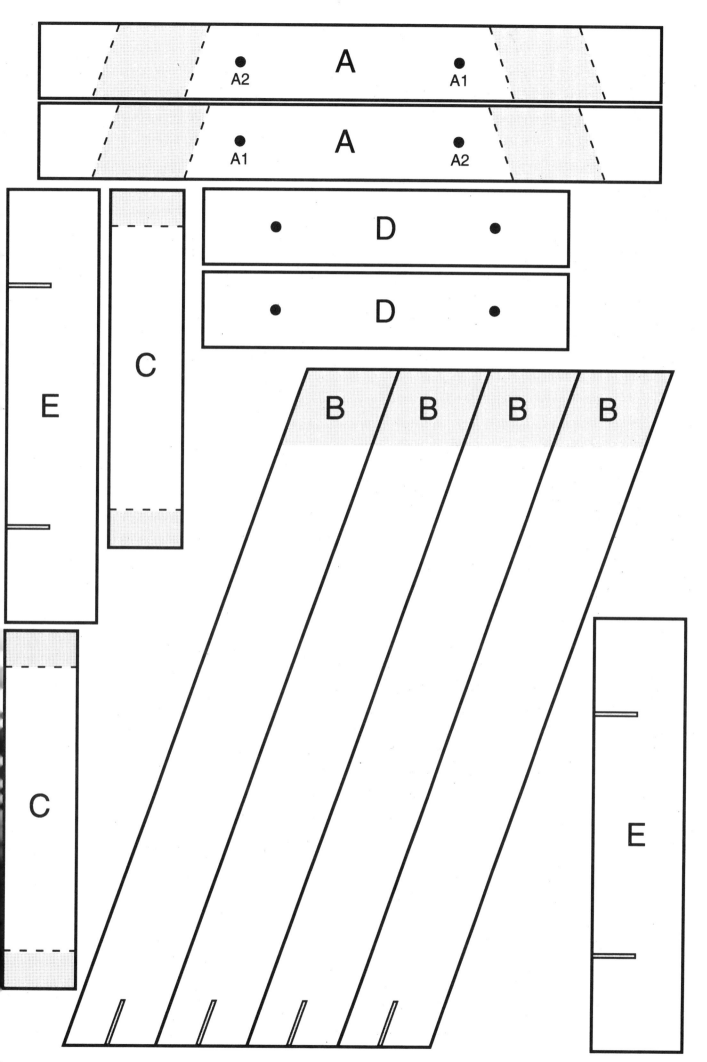

Big Wheel

Technique used:

Rotational motion - Round and round motion

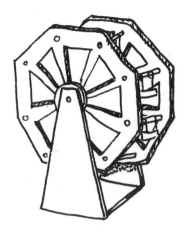

Equipment needed:

scissors	utility snips	glue
5mm dowel	round file	hole punch
paper drill	thick card	screw eyes
string	sticky tape	paints

small wheels with 4mm drilled hole

How to make the example:

Step 1. Photocopy the sheet opposite twice, 2 copies per group of children.

Step 2. Cut out the pieces from the photocopies and glue onto thick reclaimed card. Cut the card to the size of the shapes and cut out the triangles from the wheel.

Step 3. Decorate the pieces and allow to dry. Use designs inspired by fairground art.

Step 4. Punch holes through the 2 black dots marked B on the side supports and through the black dots on the wheel, the one marked A and the 8 around the edge.

Step 5. Using a round file, enlarge the holes punched through A and B to allow the dowel to be free moving.

Step 6. Cut 8 pieces of dowel to 4cm in length and glue one end of each piece of dowel into the holes around the edge of one of the sides of the wheel.

Step 7. Place the rings of two screw eyes onto each piece of dowel. These will form the attachments for the swings.
(Alternatively, bend open paper-clips.)

Step 8. Glue the second side of the big wheel on to the ends of the dowel as in the diagram.

Step 9. Cut a piece of dowel 8cm in length and place it through the holes in the centre of the big wheel. It must be free moving.

Step 10. Fold the 2 side supports of the ride along the broken lines and apply glue to one of the shaded areas.

Step 11. Place the unglued shaded area of one side support onto the glued shaded area of the second support creating a secure base for the ride.

Step 12. Place the wheel into the middle of the side supports, threading the two ends of the dowel through the holes marked B. The dowel must be free moving. Secure the dowel in place by attaching a small wheel onto each end as in the diagram.

Step 13. Cut 8 pieces of card 3cm x 1cm and punch 2 holes through the card as in the diagram.

Step 14. Attach 2 pieces of thread to each screw eye on the ride, using sticky tape as in the diagram below and knot the other end of the strings through the holes in the swing seats. This will create a free moving seat which will always remain horizontal.

How the idea may be developed:

The photocopy can be enlarged to create a bigger ride. Can the pupils create their own big wheel using the same principle? Can the ride be powered by a free falling weight or pulley system? The pupils can create a motorised roundabout using construction kit e.g. Lego or Lasy Technic.

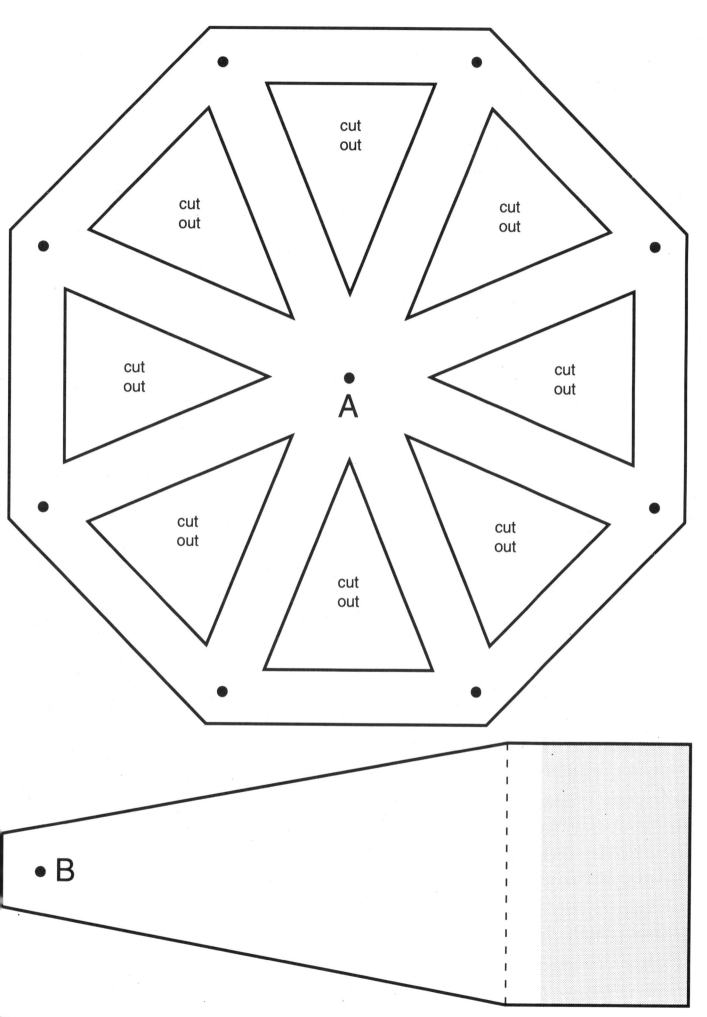

cut
out

cut
out

cut
out

cut
out

cut
out

A

cut
out

cut
out

cut
out

• B

Octopus Ride

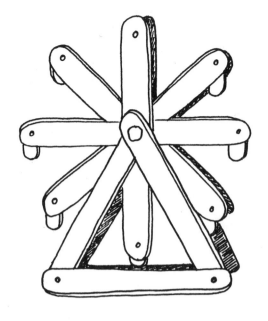

Technique used:

Joinings that allow movement
and rotational motion.

Equipment needed:

plasticene	hole punch
glue	felt pens
4mm dowel	brass fasteners
round file	paints
junior hacksaw	bench hook
utility snips	

How to make the example:

Step 1. Photocopy the sheet opposite, one per group of children.

Step 2. Glue the photocopied sheet onto thick reclaimed card and cut out the pieces.

Step 3. Punch holes through the black dots marked A - I and U - Z.

Step 4. Decorate the strips.

Step 5. Lay the 4 pieces marked AB, CD, EF and GH into a star shape as in the diagram. Glue them in place lining up the holes marked I.

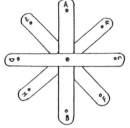

Step 6. Repeat the process with the other 4 pieces marked AB, CD, EF and GH.

Step 7. Using brass fasteners, attach the small rods marked A to H in between the arms of the two stars marked with the corresponding letters. The small rods must hang freely, if they do not then enlarge the holes with a round file.

Step 8. Using brass fasteners create 2 triangular structures using the rods marked UV, WV and WU for one and XY, ZY and ZX as in the diagram.

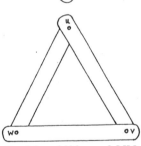

Do not place brass fasteners through the corners created by UU and XX.

Step 9. Cut a piece of dowel 5cm in length.

Step 10. Push the dowel through the 2 holes marked U, the centres of the stars marked I and finally the 2 holes marked X on the second triangular supporting structure.

Step 11. Ensure the dowel is free moving and if necessary enlarge the holes using a round file.

Step 12. Place plasticene onto the ends of the dowel to keep it in place.

Step 13. Push the arms to see the ride rotate.

Step 14. Is the ride stable? If it is not, add cross bars inbetween the two supporting structures. Test again.

How the idea may be developed:

Can the pupils create a similar fairground ride using a construction kit e.g. BrioMec, Lasy, Plastic Meccano etc.?

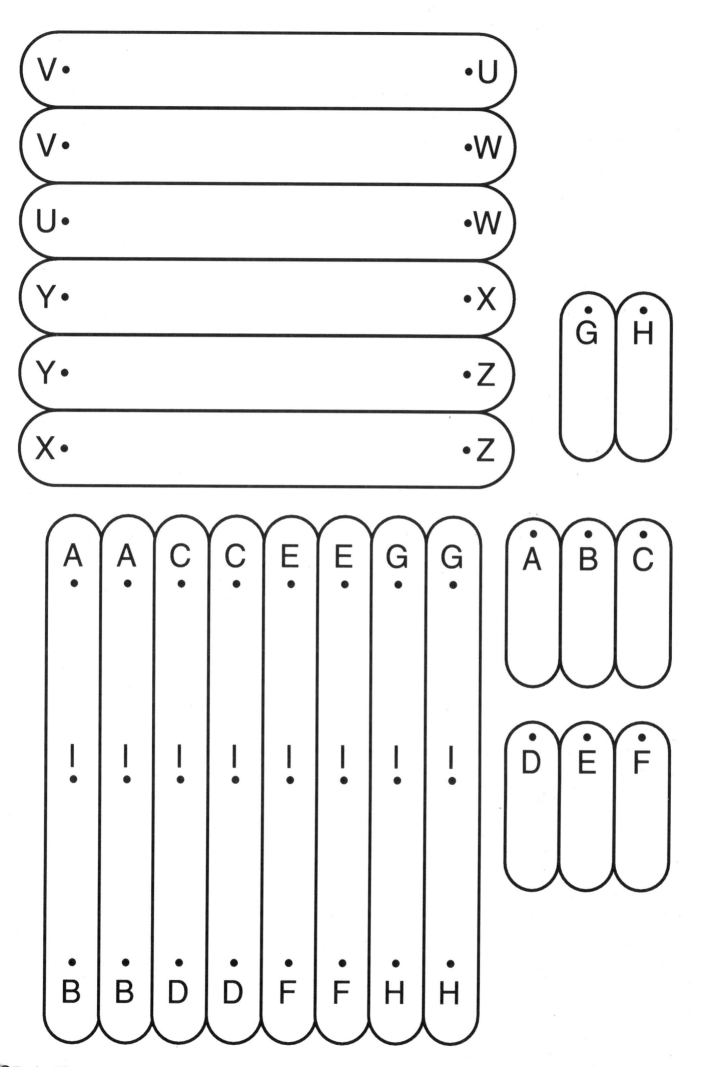

V• •U

V• •W

U• •W

Y• •X

Y• •Z

X• •Z

Ġ Ḣ

A A C C E E G G

Ȧ Ḃ Ċ

! ! ! ! ! ! ! !

Ḋ Ė F

B B D D F F H H

Umbrella Ride

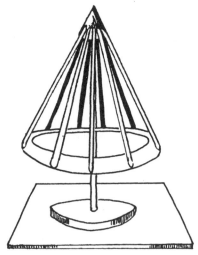

Technique used:

Tight fit dowel

Equipment needed:

> 5mm dowel
> low melt glue gun   paints
> junior hacksaw   pva glue
> lolly sticks   bench hook
> mdf or wooden wheels   small bead or plasticene
> with 4mm hole   square of thick card 15cm x 15cm

How to make the example:

Step 1. Photocopy the sheet opposite, one per child or group of children.
Step 2. Cut out the circle shape around the solid black line.
Step 3. Cut from A to B and apply glue to the shaded area.
Step 4. Fold the unshaded section of the circle over the shaded area to form a cone as in the diagram.
Step 5. Glue 8 lolly sticks onto the cone equidistant around the edge as in the diagram.
Step 6. Cut out the 'C' shape from the photocopied sheet.
Step 7. Glue 'D' to the underside of one of the lolly sticks at the bottom edge as in the diagram and form a curved circle with the paper glueing it to the lolly sticks as it is formed. Glue 'C' to the underside of the opposite edge.
Step 8. Cut a piece of 5mm dowel to 18cms in length.
Step 9. Push the dowel into an mdf or wooden wheel with a pre drilled 4mm centre hole. The dowel should be a tight fit.
Step 10. Glue the wheel into the centre of the card base.
Step 11. Glue a small bead onto the top of the dowel, allow to dry.
Step 12. Place the cone onto the bead and push the umbrella swing.
Step 13. Once the ride has been tested, it should be decorated with paints.

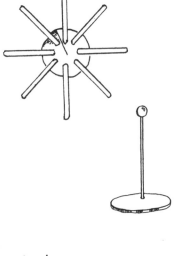

Could the children create a larger umbrella ride by working in a group? Can construction kits be used to create this type of ride? Can a different ride be made using this principle and a variety of reclaimed materials?

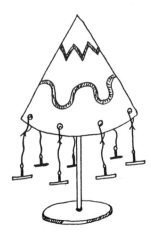

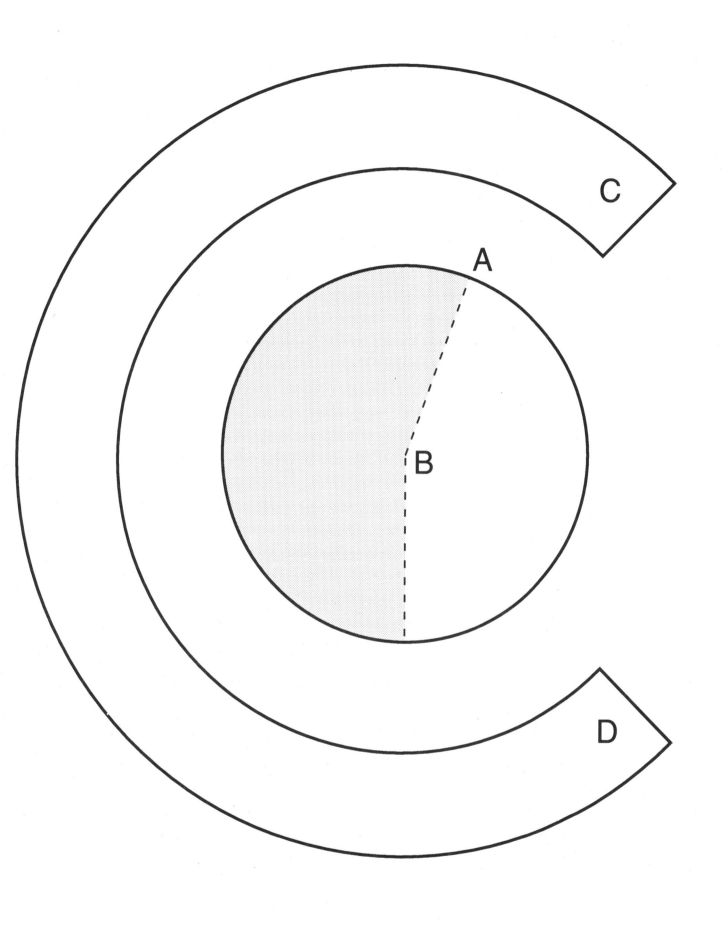

Merry - Go - Round

Technique used:
Rotational Motion - Round and round motion using pulleys.

Equipment needed:

cotton reels	low melt glue gun	bradawl
elastic bands	junior hacksaw	beads
utility snips	felt pens	paints
drill with 4mm bit	old pencils	ribbon
bench hook	thick card	hammer

wooden base approximately 30cm x 20cm.

How to make the example:

Step 1. Photocopy the sheet opposite, one per group of children.

Step 2. Cut out the shapes along the solid black lines.

Step 3. Place the circle onto thick card and draw around it. Mark the centre hole and the holes around the edge with a bradawl - Take care!

Step 4. Using a hole punch or a paper drill, make holes through the bradawl marks around the edge of the circle and through the black spots on the horses.

Step 5. Decorate the circle and the merry - go - round horses.

Step 6. Mark two black spots on the central line of the base, 17cm apart as in the diagram on the opposite page.

Step 7. Glue 2 cotton reels onto the base with the black spots showing through the centre hole, and a cotton reel in the centre of the underside of the card circle. Make sure the hole in the centre of the card circle can be seen through the central hole of the cotton reel.

Step 8. Use a complete pencil and glue the blunt end into the cotton reel on the underside of the card circle.

Step 9. Cut pieces of ribbon 20cm in length. Tie one end to the horses and push the other ends through the punched holes in the card circle. Thread a bead onto the end and knot in place as in the diagram at the top of the page.

Step 10. Cut an 8cm length of old pencill and glue it into the cotton reel on the right of the base. Place another cotton reel on top of the first one in this position.

Step 11. Place an elastic band around this second cotton reel and around a fourth cotton reel attached to the pencil glued to the card circle.

Step 12. Place this pencill into the single tier cotton reel on the left hand side of the base. The elastic band should be pulled tight. If it is not, then change it for a smaller one.

Step 13. Turn the second tier cotton reel on the right and watch the roundabout turn.

Step 14. Create a handle by drilling a tight fit hole near the edge of a wheel, place a small piece of dowel into the hole and glue the wheel onto the top of the second tier cotton reel.

How the idea may be developed:
By crossing over the elastic band, the merry - go - round can be made to travel in the opposite direction. By changing the size of the drive pulley, the speed of the merry - go - round can be altered: Smaller drive pulley = faster speed. Larger drive pulley = slower speed. Let the pupils create their own roundabout designs. What height, shape will it be? What materials will they use? Plan the sequence in which the ride will be made.

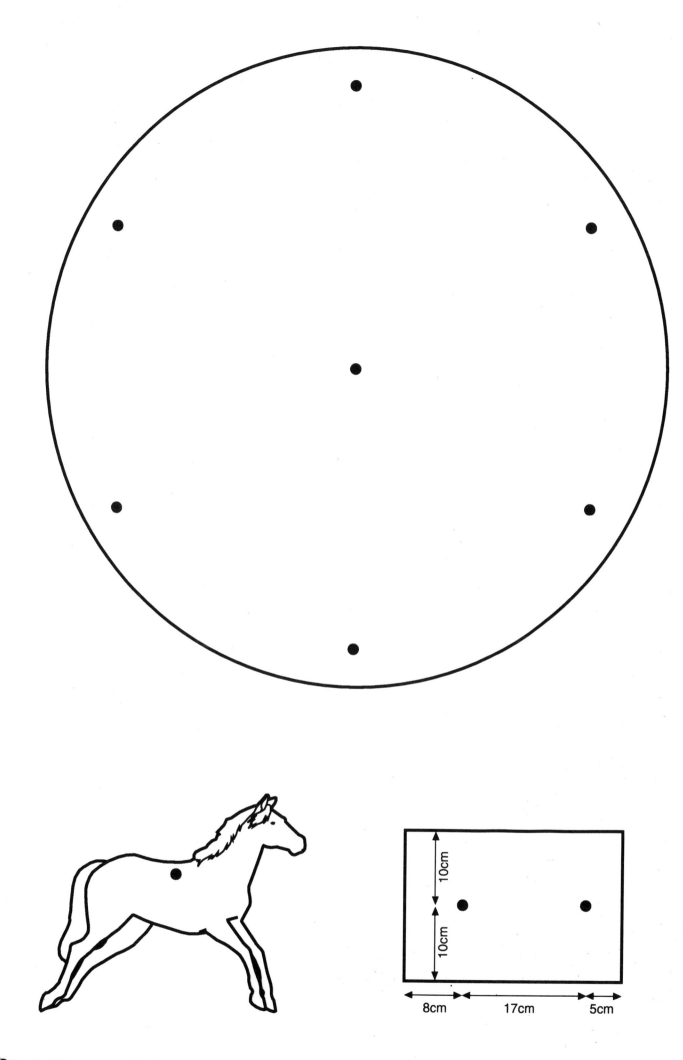

8cm 17cm 5cm

10cm

10cm

Roundabout

Technique used:
Rotational Motion using bearings.

Equipment needed:

lolly sticks	glue	
scissors	felt pens	strip wood
marbles	beads	sticky tape
5cm wheels	large elastic band	string
glue	bench hook	junior hacksaw
cardboard tube 10cm in length		low melt glue gun

How to make the example:

Step 1. Photocopy the sheet opposite, one per child or group of children.

Step 2. Cut out the shapes around the solid black lines.

Step 3. Colour the rectangular side covering of the ride which is decorated in the style of traditional fairground art and glue around the cardboard tube.

Step 4. Glue 5cm wheels onto the top and bottom of the tube using a low melt glue gun.

Step 5. Glue the photocopied base onto thick card which must be cut to the size of the base and make a hole through the centre indicated by the black spot.

Step 6. Glue the 2 strips A-B and C onto four sheet thickness card and cut to size. Decorate and fold along the broken lines. Cut down the short black lines along the bottom edge of the side pieces forming tabs.

Step 7. Place glue onto the tabs and glue them to the bottom of the base joining the strips along the shaded areas and overlapping around the base as in the diagram. **(A coffee jar lid can be used as an alternative to the card base. It is stronger and may result in a better performance.)**

Step 8. Cut 2 pieces of stripwood 8cm in length and with a low melt glue gun, attach to the base as in the diagram.

Step 9. Thread the large elastic band through the hole in the base and fix in place by placing a small piece of lolly stick through the loop.

Step 10. Thread the elastic band through the holes in the wheels on the top and bottom of the tube, use a pipe cleaner or a piece of wire as a 'needle'.

Step 11. Thread the elastic band through a large bead. The elastic band should be stretched and secured in place with a lolly stick through the loop at the top as in the diagram.

Step 12. Place 4 marbles in the base under the bottom wheel.

Step 13. Wind up the top lolly stick, release and watch the ride rotate.

How the idea may be developed:

Experiment with the number of marbles used as bearings. Try 6, 5, 4, 3, 2 and 1. Which number works the best? Create chairs as in the diagram and attach to the arms of the ride.

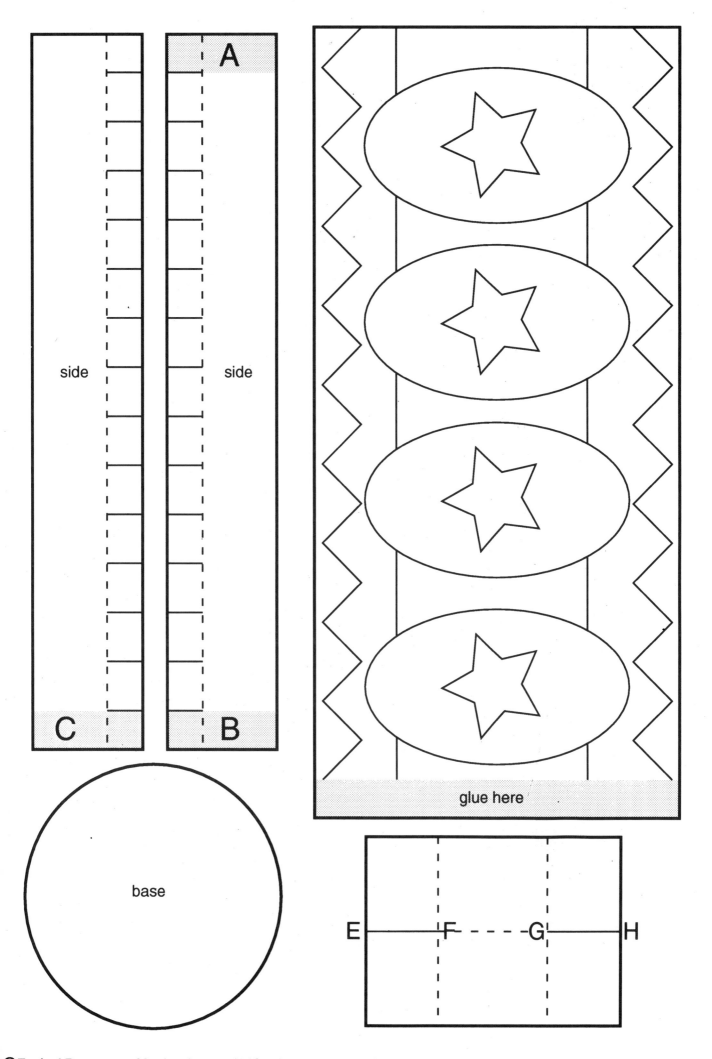

side

side

A

C

B

base

glue here

E — F --- G — H

Rising, Falling & Turning Roundabout

Technique used:

Cams

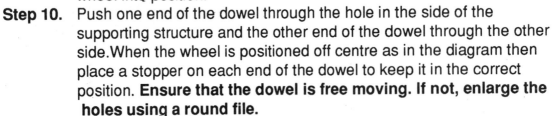

N.B.
This drawing shows
two roundabouts.
The template opposite
only makes one.

Equipment needed:

seam ripper   glue
craft knife   safety ruler
round file   felt pens
drill   bradawl
5mm dowel   low melt glue gun   scissors   corrugated plastic
3cm diamater wheels with 4mm drilled holes   utility snips   hacksaw   thick card
7cm diameter wheels with 4mm drilled holes   cutting mat   bench hook   paints

How to make the example:

Step 1.   Photocopy the sheet opposite, one per child / group of children.

Step 2.   Cut out the pieces around the solid black lines.

Step 3.   Glue the rectangle shape onto corrugated plastic or use as a template.

Step 4.   Drill holes through the position of the black dots marked A, B and C.

Step 5.   Cut through one side of the channels of the corrugated plastic in the position of the broken lines. This will enable the corrugated plastic to bend and be folded into a square as in the diagram.

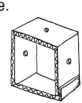

Step 6.   Using the low melt glue gun, glue the tab to the fourth side.

Step 7.   The square is not stable. Glue the small rectangular shape from the photocopied sheet onto thick card and cut out the triangle shapes. Glue 4 triangles to the front corners and 4 triangles to the back corners as in the diagram.

Step 8.   Drill a hole off centre of a wheel as in the diagram.

Step 9.   Cut a piece of dowel 9cm in length and push the wheel into the centre of the dowel. It must be a very tight fit and the wheel can be positioned easier if the dowel is placed through the central holes of a tower of cotton reels and the shaft hammered gently pushing the wheel into position.

Step 10.   Push one end of the dowel through the hole in the side of the supporting structure and the other end of the dowel through the other side. When the wheel is positioned off centre as in the diagram then place a stopper on each end of the dowel to keep it in the correct position. **Ensure that the dowel is free moving. If not, enlarge the holes using a round file.**

Step 11.   Cut a piece of felt pen barrel 2cm in length and positioning over the top hole of the structure, glue in place. This is to keep the drive shaft vertical.

Step 12.   Cut a piece of dowel 5cm in length and place down the pen barrel through the hole in the top of the supporting structure. **The dowel must be free moving.**

Step 13.   Push a 3cm wheel onto the bottom of the piece of dowel and a 7cm wheel onto the top of the piece of dowel.

Step 14.   Colour in the photocopied side for the roundabout and glue around the edge of the top wheel which is 7cm in diameter.

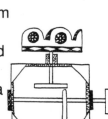

Step 15.   Drill a hole off centre of a 3cm wheel as in the diagram and push a short piece of dowel into the drilled hole to create a handle.

Step 16.   Push the centre hole of the handle onto the end of the horizontal shaft, it must be a tight fit. If it is no,t then glue the handle in place. Turn the handle and observe the motion.

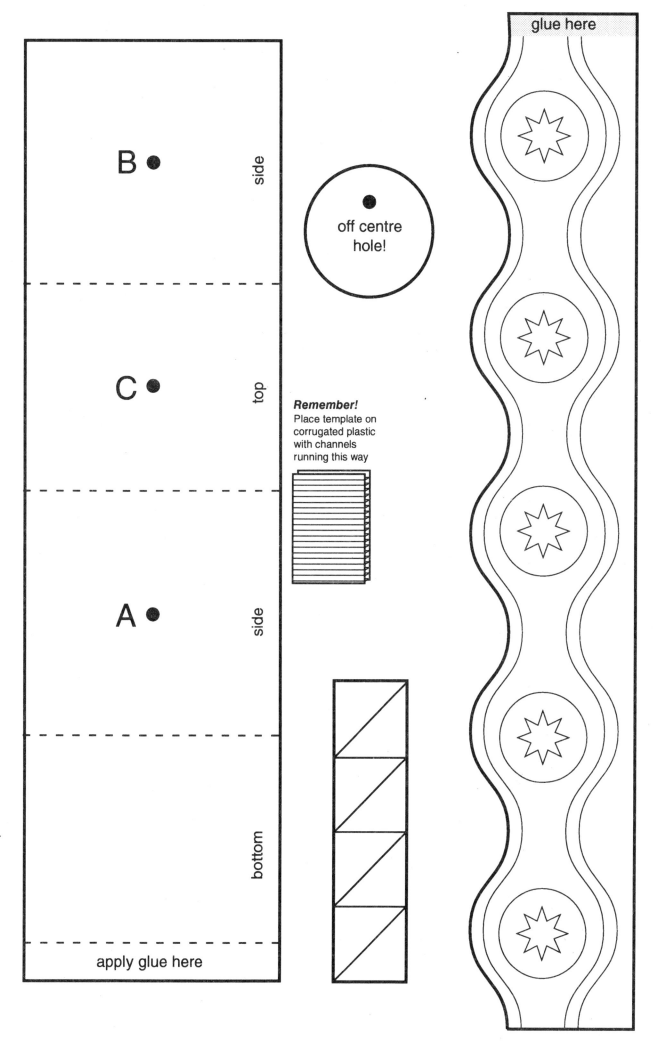

B •

side

C •

top

A •

side

bottom

apply glue here

off centre hole!

Remember!
Place template on corrugated plastic with channels running this way

glue here

glue here

Paper Drinks Container

Technique used:

Manufactured shell structure using a net.
(It will help to disassemble a real drinks carton first.)

Equipment needed:

plain white candle
coloured crayons
double sided tape
felt pens

scissors
felt pens
glue

How to make the example:

Step 1.   Photocopy the sheet opposite, one per child.
Step 2.   Cut out the drinks container along the solid black lines.
Step 3.   Fold along the broken lines and score along the triangle shapes.
Step 4.   Decorate the reverse side of the photocopied container using felt pens, wax or pencil crayons.
Step 5.   Rub vigourously over the **patterned** side with a plain wax candle ensuring all the paper is covered with the wax.
Step 6.   Rub vigourously over the **photocopied** side of the container with the wax candle ensuring all the paper is covered.
Step 7.   Re-fold along the broken lines.
Step 8.   Glue tab A under the opposite side ensuring a firm seam. Use either glue or double sided tape. Which adhesive works best?
Step 9.   Glue tab B and fold over sticking it under the opposite sides to create the rectangular base of the drinks container.
Step 10.   Fold in the 2 'V' corners and glue.
Step 11.   Fill the container with water. Is it waterproof?
Step 12.   Tip out the water and fold the top edge, glueing in place.

How the idea may be developed:

Test the strength of manufactured drinks containers. Cardboard isn't the most obvious material to use for drinks containers, how have the manufacturers waterproofed the card? You will need to disassemble the drinks containers see what the inside is like. Experiment folding, joining, shaping, rolling and scoring card of varying thicknesses. Disassemble some containers and examine the nets that create them. Use a computer program to create a logo or advertisement for the side of a carton. Test manufactured containers to see how well they pour. How well does your drinks container pour?

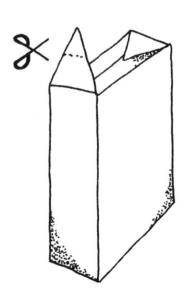

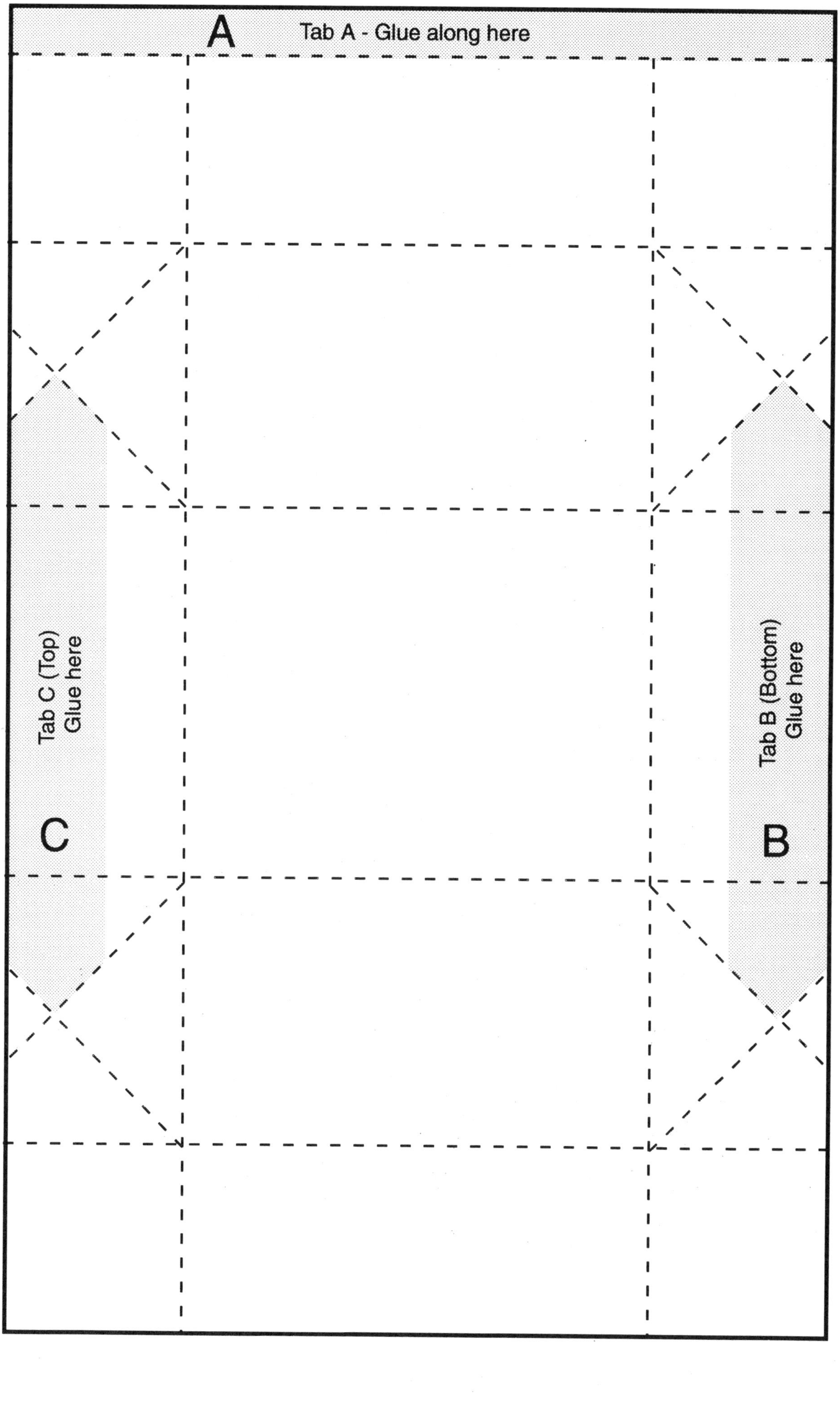

A   Tab A - Glue along here

Tab C (Top)
Glue here

C

Tab B (Bottom)
Glue here

B

Tab A - Glue along here

Fairground Art

Fairground Art is very decorative and bright, full of vibrant colours and bold designs. The boards around and above the rides should be decorated with stripes, scrolls, curves, 2D shapes and zig zags all in clashing colours with bold outlining. The lettering on the rides can be created using a word processor. Carefully cut out the letters and apply them to the models. The letters can then be highlighted with felt pens , paints or coloured crayons.Mirror work can be incorporated into the designs and sticky backed foil is easily obtained from Educational Suppliers. Sequins and glitter can be added to roundabouts to give them extra sparkle and excitement as the rides revolve.Because of the repetitive use of 2D and 3D shapes on wheels, posts and border panels, squared and isometric paper can be used to develop designs. Coloured posters, pictures and videos of traditional fairground rides can ·be shown to the children to help stimulate their own designs and ideas.